The
Long
Goodbye

The Long Goodbye

P. J. PARKER

hardie grant books

Remember when thistles danced on fairy wings—
and we could ride on rainbows?

For my mother with love ... and for my father too.

Published in 2016 by Hardie Grant Books

Hardie Grant Books (Australia)
Ground Floor, Building 1
658 Church Street
Richmond, Victoria 3121
www.hardiegrant.com.au

Hardie Grant Books (UK)
5th & 6th Floor
52–54 Southwark Street
London SE1 1UN
www.hardiegrant.co.uk

A Cataloguing-in-Publication entry is available from the catalogue of the
National Library of Australia at www.nla.gov.au
The Long Goodbye
ISBN 9781743791363

Cover design by Kate Barraclough
Text design and typesetting by Patrick Cannon
Printed by McPherson's Printing Group, Maryborough, Victoria

The paper this book is printed on is certified against the
Forest Stewardship Council® Standards. FSC promotes
environmentally responsible, socially beneficial and
economically viable management of the world's forests.

Contents

Author's note

There is little recognition that the death of a parent is a major milestone in adult life, and the death of an elderly parent is somehow seen as even less important: it's normative, expected. But it doesn't matter how old they are—how old you are—it is the parent of your youth and childhood memories lying in that casket; a curtain is being closed on more than one lifetime of hopes and dreams and love.

These memories are closest to my heart. I let them be my guide ...

P.J. Parker, 2016

Prologue

October 2012

Dial tone.

'Good evening. Charters Towers Psychology.'

'I need to talk to someone but ... I'm concerned about confidentiality.'

'Our files are strictly confidential—'

'I'm talking about ... a crime.'

'You're concerned about mandatory reporting?'

Silence, speak for me.

'We have to report if someone is in danger, at risk—or if it's a crime of a sexual nature.'

No! No! No! Not guilty! 'Can I make an appointment?'

'Just one thing ...' Timely caution. 'If our records were to be subpoenaed by a judge ...'

Fuck. Hang up!

So, here I am, dead mouthpiece in my hand, dead mouthpiece in my head ...

I look above the kindling flame, and am unnerved to find my eyes regarding me from the mirror above the hearth. It seems strangely fitting, this outline of a disembodied head communing with vacant air: *Your mother is dead ...*

From somewhere far away, the hall clock is doling out more hours, but I have slipped between heartbeats into a silence and a stillness inexpressible. In every lick of flame, ghosts are clamouring to be heard: a child feeding gidgee to an old wood stove, climbing a splintered staircase, playing hopscotch on a garden path of coloured stones ... fragments of memory ... that have led me to this point and place in time ... *my mother is dead, my father killed her.*

1

Up ya bum!

1968

Sunday morning.

The breakfast rush is on.

The doors opened at six thirty so Mum can catch the rodeo boys.

The ringers from Dotswood Station and The Star have come in for the Easter rodeo; the cafe is loud with voices, tramp of boots and Slim Dusty.

Mum is busy at her fully fired-up griller; it's a shining square of stainless steel, lit by yard-long burners. The old wood stove is bubbling tubs of fat, and a four-ring gas burner is simmering Mum's secret-recipe spaghetti sauce she got from Vince the Italian bloke, who used to own the cafe.

Caroline appears at the curtained entrance. 'Two steak-chips, two sausage, one bacon, two scrambled, one poached.'

'That's the last of the sausages, love,' Mum calls over her shoulder. 'We're out.'

Caroline is a lanky, fair-haired girl. She's one of Mum's best girls. She pins her order above the sandwich table. Mum won't read it. My mum remembers everything: today she'll cook up a hundred meals, some with none of *this*, some with double *that*.

Caroline dodges three young men come to the curtain. Cowboy hats in hand, their belts sport big shiny buckles with bucking bulls and broncos, and their boots are carved with wild mustangs too. The ringers all come out to the kitchen to say g'day to Mum.

'G'day, Mum.'

'G'day, Bernie.' Mum doesn't look up from her griller. My mum's cracking eggs into silver rings with one hand, other hand flipping bacon.

Bernie grins. 'How'd ya know it was me?'

Mum shoulders sweat from her face. 'Steak, nine eggs sunny-side up? Could only be you, Bernie,' she says, squishing sausages till they split and sizzle.

The Mosman boys think they're Mum's favourites. And I suppose the Mosman brothers are special: Tony, first to ride Powder Puff to time; Bernie, master of the bullock ride; and young Jimmy's got his heart set on being Australian Buckjump Champion one day.

Jimmy sees me gawking, winks.

I dip my head. I pretend I didn't see him. I'm sitting at the back door of the kitchen. I'm on the step that leads to the storerooms: our new home, *just for now*. 'Just for now' means until Dad helps some men build our real new house. Just for now, I got two metal buckets at my feet. In one, the water's muddy brown with spud dirt; the other's nearly full with potatoes. Just for now, I'm peeling spuds for Mum's lunch rush.

The Mosman boys are in the way when Helen comes running. Helen's the prettiest girl I've ever seen. She's a half-caste, and one of Mum's best girls. Mum's known Helen's family forever. When my mum was little, her name was Olive Chapman. Little Ollie

Chapman lived far out in the bush and had a black cook and black maids from the Gugu-Badhun tribe, and her only friends were piccaninnies.

Helen's carrying a tray of used crockery, but the wash-up table is a jumble of egg-smeared plates, tea-stained cups and coffee-pots.

Jimmy takes the tray, slides it under the table where the floor is cluttered too.

Helen pins her order, says, 'Two steak, bacon-egg, mince burger to go.'

My mum won't read it. My mum remembers everything.

The shelves are almost empty. Usually, you'd find columns of white dinner plates and bread-and-butter plates up there. And on the top shelf, cups and saucers and two-cup, four-cup, six-cup tea- and coffee-pots; only the eight-cup teapot is up there now.

I leave the potato bucket for the wash-up sinks.

Mum lifts fat-dripping bacon off the griller. 'Wriggle yourself!'

Mum's talking to the new girl. She's fourteen. She's on trial. New girl's buttering toast and bringing the plates to Mum. New girl's got mascara leaking down her face. If she wants to be one of Mum's girls, she'll have to wash her hair. And wear a longer skirt. My dad doesn't like miniskirts—or mascara—but Mum's good with bad girls. People say my mum can turn a bad girl into a good girl overnight.

I scrape T-bones into metal bins full to overflowing, pounce on a piece of pork sausage, wipe off tomato sauce—Puss doesn't like tomato sauce—and put it with my stash I got hidden under the sinks.

'More wood for the stove, love,' Mum says to me.

I go out the back to the woodheap and pick a block of gidgee— one big enough to burn for a long time and small enough to fit in the stove door.

Fire stoked, I take a quick peek through the kitchen curtain.

Slim Dusty's telling how it's lonesome at night, when wild dingoes call …

Out there are seven tables with plastic tablecloths, and one long one. Opposite the lolly counter are four booths with red vinyl seats. In the afternoons, long-haired louts and layabouts sit at those booths. They stick wads of chewy under the tables, and stand around the jukebox drinking Bodgie's Blood, puffing Marlboros and playing 'Viva Las Vegas' and 'All You Need Is Love', while teeny-bopper tarts in miniskirts tap ash from Alpine and Kool, and smile at the mirrored wall pretending Dusty Springfield: 'You don't have to say you love me …'

Wish I was Dusty Springfield.

Today, the booths are full of ringers and cowboys three deep at the counter and Slim singing about a pub that's got no beer. Mum's other best girl is out there. Her name is Helen too. This Helen is blonde. She's taking takeaway orders and whizzing milkshakes in metal tumblers.

My dad is in the front. Mr Fred Bagnall, in dress shirt and shorts and long socks, is skewering chickens on the rotisserie at the front counter because Mum says the smell of roasting chicken always gets 'em in.

My big sister's gonna baste the birds with melted butter. Her name is Robyn and she's just turned seventeen. Robyn's pretending she doesn't know she's being gawked at by all the rodeo boys.

Betty is clearing tables. Betty is thirteen and the middle sister.

And there's me: Pammie, the baby.

My sisters like working in the cafe. My sisters like the busyness and the boys.

Me? Not so much.

I drop the curtain on good ol' Slim, and his fire of gidgee coal.

'Here, love,' Mum says, handing me a swatter.

I crawl under the table. I don't like killing flies. We learned at Sunday school it's wrong to kill God's creatures. But I don't mind being under the table. I like being *out-of-the-way, love* while the rush is on. I like watching the busy feet and listening to the griller sizzle, toast pop and knives and forks clatter as Mum's girls prepare trays for their orders.

'Betcha two bob to a butcher's bum cafe down the street isn't packed.'

Everyone comes to Mum's.

It's a rude word: *Bum!*

I'm not allowed to say it ... *Bum! Bum! Bum!*

Up your bum, with a bottle of rum, chum!

My mum showed those bank managers. My mum showed 'em all!

*

December 1964 BC (Before Cafe)

Olive smoothed her skirt and crossed her ankles.

Weary *click-click* of ceiling fan; impatient *flick-flick* of Mr E.R. Salman's index finger, fretting the corner of the application paper:

Frederick Francis Bagnall, 46, Railway Worker

Olive May Bagnall, 36, House Wife

Loan Request: 2000 pounds

Collateral: Family Home

Mr E.R. Salman smoothed the creased corner and leaned back in his chair. Mr E.R. Salman laced his fingers across his stomach, and his thumbs chased each other as he studied Mr and Mrs Bagnall above his half-moon spectacles. 'Oh, dear! Oh, dearie, dearie me!'

Seeing herself through Mr E.R. Salman's eyes, Olive felt a trickle of perspiration run down her back. What was she doing here? A silly little bush girl in homemade clothes, cheap new shoes and laddered stockings, gloved hands nervously toying with a red plastic handbag.

Silly! Silly! Silly!

Mr E.R. Salman's eyes fell on Mr Fred Bagnall.

Mr Fred Bagnall took the hat from his knee and began tumbling it between his hands.

Coming to a decision, Mr E.R. Salman stood, moved around the desk. 'I'm sorry, Mr Bagnall,' he said, extending a professional hand. 'It would be unprofessional to approve such a loan.' A perfunctory clasp and shake. 'Your wife has no real experience, you see …' A conciliatory hand against her back. 'And to put your home up as collateral would be foolish.' He flicked a sleeve, glanced at his watch. 'You'll thank me in the long run.'

Blinking against the glare of Gill Street, shimmering in a hot, dry December, Olive felt her husband's humiliation: dismissed for a second time in as many hours. The New South Wales Bank manager hadn't even interviewed them; he'd cancelled last minute: 'I'm sorry.' A young man had handed back their application. 'You don't have a telephone, so we couldn't let you know.'

'Well.' Fred brushed imaginary lint from his new fedora. 'Guess that's that.'

'No experience!' Olive said tightly, taking him by the elbow. 'Come on.'

'Where are we going?'

'To try the Commonwealth!'

*

1968

The cafe is a double-storey building on the main street of Charters Towers.

The second storey is condemned, but I sneak up there sometimes. The staircase is rickety; two treads are missing, and you have to take a really big step across a splintered landing. It's vast and bare up there. Dust motes are suspended in rays of sunlight, cobwebs hang from roof beams, and little dunes of dust show signs of rodent scuttle.

It used to be a dance hall, up there. Listen carefully, you can hear a saxophone and the fading echo of an accordion. Behind the beams of dust, ol' Donny McCloud is sitting at his drums, head nodding to the steel tap of his brushes. Long gowns sweep sawdust along the floor, and ankles flash beneath daring hemlines as a few brave souls show off the Turkey Trot and the Bunny Hug to celebrate the beginning of a new century.

My dad, Mr Fred Bagnall, says that in 1900 Charters Towers had a lot to celebrate. In just twenty-eight years, the town had grown from virgin bush to 27,000 people; there were twenty crushing batteries and seventy-five cyanide plants producing record yields of gold. In those days, the Towers was the most prosperous community in Australia; it was called 'The World'. Nowadays, 'The World' is just a dozy little bush town, population 8000—only claim to fame the Charters Towers Goldfield Ashes. They say our amateur cricket carnival, held on the Australia Day long weekend, will one day be the largest in the Southern Hemisphere.

On one wall up there, a rusty nail holds a tattered poster. It's got a faded lion standing upright on a cricket pitch; he's carrying a bat on one shoulder and wearing a cap made from the Union Jack. Gathered all around the lion are kangaroos wearing Aussie slouch hats. Some of the words are impossible to read now, but the umpire is saying: *You've done jolly well,* [text missing] *cricket fields, and now you're going to federate at home. Bravo, boys!*

I like wearing my dad's slouch hat. One side of the brim is pinned up with a Rising Sun Badge so you can carry a rifle slung over one shoulder. My dad didn't go AWOL, so he wasn't rounded up and sent to New Guinea in a cage, and doesn't have a war medal like my Uncle Jack does.

At the front of the cafe, four tall windows are boarded up but you can look down at Gill Street through the slits of metal louvres. While the morning sun's still pushing shadows along the street, I sometimes see the gutter-man down there. He pushes a wire broom in front of him, chasing slimy water down the catchment drains. I sometimes see Stanley Whorton down there, collecting the papers for his paper run. Stanley walks with one leg swinging out, and keeps one arm tucked up like a chicken wing. Mum says Stanley Whorton was born that way—*You shouldn't mock him, love*—but kids say Stanley is a spastic and that's why they mock him.

You have to be early to catch Mrs Patterson in her buggy. Mrs Patterson is an old witch more than a hundred years old. She slaps the reins at a big grey horse, *clip-clop, clip-clop*, and flicks her whip at little kids if you want to pat her horse. 'Goaon!' Mrs Patterson yelled at me. 'Git awy wit ye, ya little begga!' Mrs Patterson's is the only buggy you'll see on the streets of Charters Towers nowadays. One time Mrs Patterson's old grey horse did a poop walking down the main street, and the old horse just kept on walking and pooping till halfway down the street, and the gutter-man waved his broom at her and yelled, 'Go on, get outta the main street!' and Mrs Patterson flicked her whip at the gutter-man and the gutter-man ran onto the footpath and shook his broom and yelled, 'I'm goin' ta report ya! An' ya horse! Ya bloody ol' witch!' The gutter-man must've reported the old witch and her horse, because Mrs Patterson's not allowed to let her horse poop in Gill Street anymore.

It's good watching the early sun fall on the shuttered eyelids of the shops: *Time to wake up!* The shops yawn and blink: awnings roll out over footpaths, and blinds roll up on window displays. I like watching the first cars coming and going, and, later, little people with brown paper grocery bags stopping to read the billboards: *FRI* and *SAT NIGHT* at the Regent Picture Theatre. At night, my mum keeps her cafe open till interval at the pictures. At nine o'clock, and later if the talkies are running late, layabouts and little tarts run across the street for hamburgers and cigarettes—and Jaffas for chucking when the lights go down.

A metallic rattle and clank tells me it's two o'clock, and the doors are shutting. There was a time, BC—Before Cafe—when Sunday mornings meant church and Sunday school, where we learned that God sees everything we do, and that we deserved a sharp slap with a ruler if we didn't kneel up straight. Father Guy's wife kept a sharp eye on sinners, and little kids kneeling straight. Mum used to take us to church on Sunday morning. Not anymore. Mum's cafe is open seven days a week, and my mum's always busy.

Still, if I had to choose between two bob and a butcher's bum, I'm glad my mum showed those two bank managers wouldn't loan her for the cafe lease—and the one who did.

*

December 1964 BC

'Don't let Lucky jump up, Pammie!' Mum swats my puppy with her glove. 'Look what he's done! And that's the second time today!' She hitches her skirt, sits down on the bed, unclips suspender tabs front and back from her step-ins, rolls down the laddered stocking and tosses it into the bottom of the cupboard. 'The bank man will be here any minute,' my mum says, rummaging in her underwear drawer. 'Take Lucky outside, love.'

Mum wasn't expecting the bank man to come today. Mum wasn't expecting the man to follow them home in his car.

I try to catch Lucky, but Lucky jumps onto Mum's bed and digs a hiding place in the quilt. I get Mum's laddered stocking and tie it to his collar. Lucky is my little black and tan puppy I found in the long grass beside the highway. Mum said, 'We'll call him Lucky,' because my mum says he's lucky to be alive.

'Hurry up, Ollie!' Dad is holding the curtain back, looking out the window.

Mum leans into the mirror and shapes her lips like an O is for Olive.

'Come on, Ollie!' says Dad. 'He's here!'

Mum grabs a petticoat from the drawer, clamps her lips on it—once, twice—pushes it with red lip marks back into the drawer. Mum looks lovely in her new dress. She finished making it this morning on her Singer sewing machine. Her dress is navy blue with little white polka dots; the skirt comes halfway down her leg and there's a split up one side just past the knee. I admire my reflection in the mirror. I love the navy-blue, white-polka-dot knickerbockers my mum ran up for me from leftovers. Mum slips her feet into her new red stilettos and smooths her skirt.

I bring Lucky and follow them outside.

Our home is Number 38, Mount Leyshon Road, Charters Towers. Our home is on the fork of Mount Leyshon Road and the highway. Goat country, Dad calls it. But our home is bordered by a white picket fence, and outside the fence is a wide strip of gravel to hold back long brown grass and goats.

The bank man gets out of his car. He's a big man in a suit and tie. He leans through the window to get a clipboard and his hat. He puts the hat on his head and the clipboard under one arm, and he looks at our house for a long time before coming over to the picket gate where Mum and Dad are waiting. They shake hands and nod and smile.

The bank man walks down one of Dad's sanded paths and runs his fingers along the pointy tops of the picket fence. My dad found the wood for that picket fence at the abandoned American air-force base at Breddon. He cut and painted every picket and put them up on a border of dark green cement. My dad's good with cement. He adds coloured powder to the mixer, and the cement pours out green.

Dad follows the bank man, but the path is only wide enough for two and Mum is wondering if she should walk with them. Mum's eyes are smiling. Mum shrugs at me and holds up both hands, fingers crossed.

I smile and shrug and hold up my crossed fingers too.

Mum goes inside to put the kettle on. I follow Dad, but I keep my distance because I don't want to be chased inside. Dad and the man walk along Dad's garden beds and admire the bright leaves of Dad's crotons. Dad's like a policeman directing traffic, showing the bank man where he's going to put a line of eight royal palms.

They walk across the lawn to the pergola. Dad built that pergola from lattice he found out at the American air-force base at Breddon. It's got dark green vines climbing up the sides and pink flowers hanging over the cement pond my dad made where our goldfish swim. Around the pond there's a little iron rod fence Dad found at the base at Breddon so I won't drown.

'I know where I've seen this!' says the bank man. 'I saw the photo in the *Northern Miner*. Winner of the garden competition last month? It took me a minute to put it together, but you're *the* Fred Bagnall? I've read your letters in the paper!'

Dad looks pleased.

At the side fence, the man looks across the spear grass and up at Towers Hill. You don't see many trees around the Towers, except the thorny Chinee apple; the good trees were all cut down for shoring up mine shafts or burning in the boilers. Dad points out what's left of the red-brick pyrites tower. It was pulled down during World War II. Dad tells how Towers Hill hides more than twenty old mine shafts and more than forty bunkers built by the RAAF during the war to store bombs and parachute flares.

Dad knows all the stories, but even I could tell about Jupiter Mosman. How on a Christmas Eve nearly a hundred years ago the little black boy found a big nugget of gold in one of those wash-off gullies on Towers Hill, and how concentrated-vein gold made Charters Towers the richest major goldfield in Australia.

Dad and the man follow the cement path along the front of the house and step along Dad's green, red and yellow step-n-stones that lead up to our veranda. Our veranda's made of polished red cement. It's got steel in it that Dad picked up out at Breddon.

Dad follows the man through the house and the man says, 'Lovely home, Mrs Bagnall.' Then the man follows Dad into the laundry. My mum's got a washing machine. It's got two rollers to squash water out. I'm not allowed near the rollers so I won't get my hand mangled. Our house hasn't got a back door. The Americans didn't leave any doors lying round at Breddon, but Dad's going to put on a back door just as soon as he finds one.

The man looks along the highway that heads out to the Belyando Crossing. You often see hitchhikers standing on the road outside our house. Some people call them hoboes or swaggies, but Dad says not to worry, they're just men headed south looking for work at the mines in Clermont or Emerald. The swaggies hitch a lift with the big cattle trucks that thunder past our house. Sometimes a swaggie arrives in the early morning and at midday he moves in under the shade of our peach tree hanging over that fence—you don't get good peaches off that tree, just little hard ones and you got to eat round the worms—and at dusk you can still see the swaggie's shadow and the burning tip of a cigarette glowing in the dark. Sometimes I think Mum is frightened when Dad's working night shift at the railway and there's no back door at our house, but she never says so.

Out the back, Dad's planted a row of pines to block off the back garden from the backyard. There's a big sandpit, a yellow swing set and a slippery slide. I tie Lucky to the slide, climb the ladder and slide down three times to show the bank man I'm not scared, but the bank man's looking at Dad's carrots, beets and lettuce. I climb onto a swing and swing really high. One day, my cousin Jackie wouldn't stop swinging on the swing even though I told her to stop because I wanted to slide down the slippery slide, so I slid down anyway and a bolt in the bottom of Jackie's swing hit me in my head and Mum and Dad wrapped my head in towels and took me to the hospital, and good ol' Doc Ellis put nine stitches in my head and I didn't bleed to death.

In the back corner of our backyard is the outhouse. Our outhouse is yellow and blue. There's an electric light bulb inside. Mum and Dad rode their bikes twelve mile in the dark, all the way out to the army base at Breddon, to get the electric cable Dad connected to the house. The light switch for the outhouse is in the laundry. It's not scary in the daytime, but at night it's a long dark way to get up to the dunny. There are shadows outside the torch beam and sometimes a rustle in the leaves or grass. If I need to go at night I say, 'Does anyone want to go to the lavatory, because I'm going now.' But one time Dad came out of the bathroom saying, 'Which one of you girls peed in the bath?' And I said, 'Betty did!' Dad looked at me till I said, 'And I did too,' but Betty got a harder smack than I got because Betty *should know better!*

Back on the front veranda, the bank man sits on one of our cane chairs. Our cane chairs didn't come from the dump because Dad picked them up for two bob at an auction sale. Mum brings out a pot of tea and fruitcake.

Everyone seems happy when the bank man stands up and shakes Dad's hand. The bank man shakes Mum's hand too and says, 'I've seen all I need to see. Come in tomorrow and I'll have the paperwork ready.'

Before the car has disappeared down the road Mum is hugging Dad, and Mum hugs me too. 'I'll show them!' my mum says.

And she did: Mum showed those two bank managers wouldn't loan her for the cafe lease—and the one who did: the loan approved by the Commonwealth Bank late in December '64 was paid in full by Christmas '65.

*

1968

Whenever you hear the rattle of the cafe doors closing at the end of the day, Mum will be spreading handfuls of caustic soda on the cement floor of the kitchen. No matter what time—Sunday afternoon or late at night—Mum scrubs the kitchen with boiling water and a wire broom. Out the front, there are brooms sweeping, cloths wiping, mops mopping; the counter fridge is restocked with Whitbreads Cordials; two-gallon ice-cream buckets are replaced in the deep freeze, and the cigarette stand and baskets of Samboy chips and Twisties are refilled.

My big sister is making eyes at a ringer down by the counter. Greg looks about the same age as Robyn, seventeen, maybe eighteen. He's got brown hair, big brown eyes and big, big sideburns. Sideburns are all the fashion nowadays. He's a good-looking fella but I don't like him. I miss Robyn's old boyfriend. It's much too soon for a new boyfriend in our family.

Tell 'im to go! Can't he see we're shut?

Robyn takes a set of keys from the till, opens the big chrome door of the jukebox and kneels to push the button inside. Mum always lets her girls play free music while they work. Robyn and Greg run their fingers down the list of songs and they argue and jostle shoulders. The wheel of 45s spins and an automatic arm comes down with a click, lifts A4 onto the turntable and Lulu sings about how her school days are gone and how it isn't easy to thank someone but she'll tryy-i-i-yi.

Greg gives Helen money for a bottle of Coke and he tries to give the Coke to me. I fold my arms behind my back, shake my head *I don't like Coke* and run back into the kitchen, where Mum's slamming plates through the rinse sinks. My middle sister, Betty, is folding paper napkins and stamping them with purple ink: *Tropical Cafe* beneath two coconut palms on a tiny island. *Monday to Saturday: 9 am–9 pm. Sunday: 9 am–2 pm.*

I crawl under the table and set about punishing flies for annoying Mum. I trap them in two cupped hands. I carefully roll them along my palm. You gotta get 'em between thumb and forefinger to pull their wings off without squashing them.

Mum's face appears under the table. 'Hop out, love. I'm going to do the floors.'

'See what I done, Mum?' I say, herding nine flies between my hands. 'I pulled off their wings, so I don't have to kill 'em.'

'That's a cruel thing to do!' Mum says, passing me the fly swatter. 'But, Mum!'

'Only a nasty little girl would let them crawl around like that!' Mum starts spreading caustic soda, but all I know is my mum's never spoken to me like that before, all stern and disappointed. 'Don't cry, love,' Mum says. 'But you can't leave them without wings. Go on!'

Poor flies don't stand a fighting chance, and I didn't wanna kill 'em.

'Afta-nooon!' Lenny's the pigman—he breeds pigs on his farm. Lenny's as skinny as a scarecrow, and his voice creaks and cracks. 'Busy t'daaay … Mrs Baagnall?' He hoists the heavy scrap bins onto bony shoulders, and squeaks, 'Still havin' trouble … with them toms, Mrs Baaagnall?'

Mum goes to the back door, sniffs, and she can smell it too: one of the wild toms that hang out in Beares' bakehouse next door has started peeing in the open gutter that runs past the back door of our kitchen. 'Fred!' Mum says. 'You're going to have to do something about those damned cats!'

I sneak my plate of scraps from under the sink and follow Lenny outside. Lenny's rattle-trap old ute is out near the woodheap. Lenny loads Mum's shiny silver bins. Other people's bins got black mucky spills all down the sides.

Up the back of the cafe is Beares' old red-brick bakehouse. Its second storey is condemned too. The windows are boarded up but most of the glass has been smashed by kids chucking rocks. It wasn't me. I can't chuck that high. On Sundays, the bakehouse is deserted except for gnarly old toms. Those old cats are in there, lying on the dough rolls that are laid out on the benches for tomorrow's bake. They eye you meanly and snarl at you on your way up to the dunny.

It's even scarier going up there in the dark than it was to our dunny at our old house. Even in the daytime the wooden door to the bakehouse dunny squeaks when you push it open, and won't close properly when you push it shut. Inside is a wooden box with a hole in the top. There's a pile of sawdust on one side to spread over number twos and a pile of old newspaper on the other side for wiping. Scariest part is sitting down on that hole ...

Lenny's ute rattles away and I crawl in under the tank stand. It's just high enough to crouch under. I *should know better!* but only God can see me, so I promise him: *Dear God, this is the last time.* I pull up my pants and scrape handfuls of dirt over the puddle I just made until it's really dry and I lie down beside it to wait for Puss.

Puss isn't like the other rickety tabbies that hang out in Beares' bakehouse. Puss is black with white stockings. She has a pretty face and her green eyes have tiny specks of brown. It's taken me a long time but, if I'm very still, Puss-in-Boots will bring her two kittens into our tank-stand hidey-hole. Yesterday, Puss took mince from my hand and when she arched her back into my other hand I could feel her motor running. Mum says, 'They're wild cats, love, you shouldn't try to tame them.' But Mum's wrong about Puss-in-Boots. Puss is almost tame; I'm the one who tamed her.

The cafe is shut, the main street empty, the Beares away for the afternoon. It's a cosy little hidey-hole surrounded by ferns; the earth is damp and cool here.

Catnapping, I lie in wait for Puss.

Sweep of broom, clank of mop on bucket.

Daydreaming of Lucky, when I hear …

Voices?

I roll onto my side, crawl into a squat and spy four manly legs passing by my hidey-hole—hands with sacks and netting?

Some mischief is afoot.

I duck my head beneath the beam and four legs become two men: dress shorts, long socks, town shoes; a pair of jeans and riding boots.

A giggle wells inside: they don't know I'm here. They don't know I'm watching.

They're heading for the woodheap.

From the pile of wood a battle-scarred old tabby is watching too. Town-cunning, the old tom knows his life is up for grabs.

The wood is hemmed on two sides by the cafe walls behind; the net is spreading when the woodheap spawns a litter! Cats.

Cats slinking, darting, leaping.

A crotchety streak of tabby catapults against a chest, ricochets away.

A grey streak feints, acrobats, climbs on air: two wily toms scarper for the bakehouse.

A tabby barrels into the netting, tumbles, tangles, climbs.

'Curses! Hold 'im, Fred!'

Puss-in-Boots appears, two wide-eyed kittens behind her.

Puss leaps. A hand snares her tail.

Puss loops into a question mark, teeth and claws clutching.

Somewhere, someone is screaming.

Too late!

Puss-on-Arm thrust in sack, pummelling, kicking, bulging.

Arm jerks, sack drops.

Puss-Latched-on-Hand-Latched-on-Throat, mouth snarled, body whip-cord taut.

Fingers clenched, fist trembling.

Paws claw, hind rakes.

I am crawled from hiding.

Someone, somewhere, is screaming.

Mum is come.

Too late!

Clamped hands twist.

Puss, jiggled on noose, eyes popped, tongue stuttering, paws jit-jit-jittering.

Mum turns me away.

I wail.

Dad gasps.

Puss dangles.

Silence.

It is done: she, who was living is dead, and …

And I hate my dad.

I hate my dad to infinity on the day he murders Puss-in-Boots.

You, my child, will hate your dad to hell and back on the day he kills your mum …

2

In the beginning

November 2012

In every tongue of flame, the woman on the outside looking in sees the child on the inside looking out:

How do you feel now? the child demands to know. *Still hate your father?*

I don't know, the woman hedges. *I remember Mum saying that he didn't mean to kill Puss-in-Boots. Once Puss had hold of him, he had no choice ...*

The child pins her to the truth. *I wasn't talking about the cat!*

I know, but ...

The memories dissipate, coalesce once more into the present smell of gidgee burning.

An empty silence reclaims the night.

Taking the poker, I prod the settling coals, watch myriad tiny sparks scintillate briefly before expiring in the grate. Embers slip into a bed of powdered ash; shadows on the walls become sedate and dwindle fitfully away.

My old house and the evening are closing their shutters on another day.

I want so much to tell the world that she lived—and died—and how such a wonderful life, lived so well, could end so badly.

But not tonight. Not yet.

Where would I begin? *On the 28th of October, my father killed my mother ...*

Expressive impulse, grinding grief and guilt and rage onto the page? An account of time and place and circumstance? What of the ochre reds of drought-parched earth, the orange dazzle of the evening sky, the blue twinkle in my mother's eye?

Beyond the window, moon glow ignites willow leaves and runs quicksilver through the branches. The air is almost still now; there's just enough movement to suggest the subtle night perfumes of red gum and ash ... the drum of hoof beats ... the smell of wood smoke ... the black and bitter taste of sweetened billy tea ...

The hall clock is doling out small hours, but beneath the mundane text of Time's ongoing tale, goodnight kisses flutter in the licorice darkness about my pillow. I crawl into an unmade bed.

I cannot wrap my arms around her. *My mother is dead.* I wrap them around myself. A hollow vessel that makes no sound. I cannot cry; even in this state of stasis, I know that my tears—when they come—will be not only for her but for me. It's hard not to be egocentric when you're so evidently, self-consciously, the centre of the universe.

*

Charters Towers: December 1963 BC

Sundee arvo and Dad's taking me over to the Paines'.

Aunty May Paine lives across the road with a TV—and Uncle Harry. Sunday night is my favourite show: *Mr Ed*. Dad likes Mr Ed, the talking horse, just as much as me, and Dad loves Fred Flintstone even more than me.

I sit cross-legged on the lino. Aunty May's lino has faded pink cabbage roses and green leaves and a track of little black holes from the front door to the kitchen where my Aunty May forgot to take off her stilettos like my mum takes off her stilettos so you don't get black holes in our lino. After *Mr Ed* and *The Flintstones*, I watch *Disneyland* while Dad's having a cup of tea. I watch the fire burn through the map of Ponderosa but the next thing I know Dad's picking me up.

'Dad, I wanna watch *Bonanza*!'

Next week, Bonanza special guest stars will be Jack Lord and Susan Oliver; stay tuned for some exciting scenes …

Bonanza is already finished. I pretend I can't wake up properly so my dad will carry me back across the road where it's dark. There aren't any streetlights this far out of town. In the light on our veranda, I see Mum's home from work. Dad lets her hug us and he sings, 'Just Ollie and me, and our baby makes three.'

My mum tucks me in my bed and I say, '*Mr Ed*'s my favourite, Mum.'

And Mum says, 'Mmmm.'

'Will you watch it with me next week?'

And Mum says, 'Mmmm.'

'How many sleeps now till Santa comes, Mum?'

'Three more sleeps till Santa. Nigh-night, love.'

'Santa didn't come to your place when you were little, did he, Mum? 'Cause you lived far out in the bush and Santa had to send presents with the mailman. And Santa didn't come to Dad's place because Santa didn't have the address … Mum, do you think Dad wanted a boy?'

'Why would you ask that?'

'It's just that Dad's only got three girls and I think Dad might like a boy. I wish I was a boy—or had a boy-sounding name like Bobby or Toni. Why'd you call me Pammie?'

'Pamela June,' says Mum, 'because I wanted a pretty name for my pretty baby girl.'

I say, 'Bagnall's not a pretty name.'

And Mum says, 'No, Bagnall's not a pretty name, but it's the only thing I didn't like about your dad so I married him anyway.'

'If you had to choose, Mum …'

'Mmm?'

'If you had to choose between Dad and me, who'd you choose?'

'I don't have to choose. I love you both very much, but you'll grow up one day, and when you're a big girl you'll go away and have children of your own, but Daddy and me will always be together.'

'But, if you really, really *had* to choose …'

'I'd choose Daddy, sweetheart, but you will always be my special girl.' Mum smooths back my fringe, kisses my forehead. 'Nigh-night, love.'

I'm glad Mum gave the right answer.

Glad, too, that one day I'll have someone all to my own.

I snuggle down in bed, and find myself thinking how seeing ol' Mr Benham leading three mules down a dusty track with the mail wouldn't be anywhere near as magic as Santa flying reindeer through the stars.

And I find myself thinking, *That's just how it was in Mum's day …*

*

Valley of Lagoons, December 1933

'He's comin', Big Minnie!' Olive yelled. 'Mailman's comin'!'

Wading through pink and purple waterlilies, Olive ran the shallows, splashing silver water in her wake. Waterfowl, beating the

22

glassy surface with their wings, lifted skyward and circled on the happy sound of Big Minnie's laughter. 'Slow down, Miss Olive!'

Kookie's *Oo-oo-ah-ahh-ahhh* chased Olive along the bank, and it seemed the whole world was laughing with him: the hot summer air shimmered with the clear music of the pied butcher bird, and the raucous screech of a red-tailed cockatoo sent a lorikeet and rosella rainbow flocking overhead as Olive ran up the slope towards the homestead.

'Mailman's comin', Mundie!' she called to the house boy.

Mundie barely spared her a grin. Mundie was busy. Most every day you'd find the old blackfella hunkered down, busy clipping the homestead lawns with his hand shears.

'Mum!' Olive leaped up the stairs, skipped across the veranda and poked her head into the main dining room. 'Mailman's—'

Her mum wasn't there, only two maids setting the table.

At the end of the veranda, Olive peeked in the window of the black girls' dining room. No one there. And no point in either poking or peeking in the stockmen's dining room—they were all gone into Ingham for the holiday.

Running into the kitchen, Olive told Skinny Minnie, 'Mailman's comin'!'

'Slow down, Miss Olive!' Skinny Minnie scolded, a big fat turkey clamped between bony knees, her black hands all feathers.

'Can't slow down!' Olive told her breathlessly. 'Mailman's comin'!'

Olive ran around the veranda and found her big sister. 'Mailman's coming! He's got *three* mules! Come on, Dulce!' she begged. *'Come on!'*

'Put your shoes on!' Dulcie said, tying a lace. 'Ground's gonna be hot.'

'Mum!' Olive shouted at the vacant sky. 'Mailman's comin'! He's nearly here!'

23

Mr Benham and his horse and mules had already passed the turn-off. Mr Benham's horse and mules were already trotting up along the track, their hooves sending little puffs of dust drifting sideways on the breeze.

Together, the girls raced, calling, 'Mr Benham!' and waving, 'Mr Benham!'

'Now, don't you girls go gettin' too het up,' Mr Benham cautioned, as they danced around the pack animals. 'Ain't no way Santa gonna send out all these presents for just two girls. By my reckonin', too many presents 'ere, for just two girls, an' a baby sister.'

'You're teasin', Mr Benham!' Olive clasped her fingers and twisted her arms inside out. 'You're just teasin', ain't ya?'

Mr Benham grumbled. 'Not many places Royal Mail hasta put on an extra mule just 'cause it's Christmas.' But there was laughter in Alfie Benham's eyes and a smile on his whiskered face as he giddy-upped the mules.

Slide-sidestep-bounce, Olive and Dulcie danced alongside, wondering, hoping.

Most every week, Mr Benham brought their correspondence lessons. The lessons taught all sorts, like numbers and letters, but they didn't need lessons to know the valley was an inland floodplain. All they needed was Big Minnie and Skinny Minnie taking them walkabout down along the springs to explore the big off-channel lakes and clear waterholes. Big Minnie and Skinny Minnie knew where to find emu eggs and bustard eggs, knew where to find the ancient rock weirs built by the Gugu-Badhun, knew how to catch fish with their hands. Just look around, they didn't need book learning to see how the Gugu-Badhun had held out against the squatters a lot longer than other blackfella tribes: they had just run into the basalt wall where the police horses couldn't follow—in the big black rocks there were caves and a hundred places where a blackfella could disappear. And, finally, they didn't need book learning to see why the northern loop of the Burdekin was called Black Burdekin: everyone knew how the bronzewing pigeon and the pheasant had had a quarrel, and how the mean old bronzewing had set fire to the valley, and that's why all the rocks were black.

'Mornin', Mrs Chapman.' Mr Benham swung down and set about unbuckling straps. 'Well, would ya look at that!' he exclaimed, taking down one of the big brown packages. 'I'm real sorry, Mrs Chapman, dunno how that could've happened!'

May Chapman grabbed the parcel and quickly held it against her chest, but Olive had caught a glimpse of a little porcelain foot poking from a tattered hole in the paper—a little porcelain foot with broken toes.

*

Charters Towers: Christmas 1964

Dolls! What did they do? What were they for?

We're sitting around a pine tree in a bucket; it's got bits of silver on it. Lucky's chasing wrapping paper and skidding on the lino. Mum's saving the big bits of paper for next year. Robyn's naming her doll Miranda. Betty's naming her doll Kathy. Miranda's got bright orange hair, a china face, stiff black eyelashes and big blue glass eyes that open and close. Kathy's got a little milk bottle—and has already wet herself. I'm calling my doll Jane, but really I'm wondering what'd be the point of being a good girl all year and praying for a pony if Santa only brings ya a stupid plastic doll.

And Mum and Dad aren't talking.

My dad is not a bad man. Dad only skinned Smokey-the-cat after Smokey went on up to heaven. Mum told how Smokey got so old and tired, Smokey asked God to take him on up to heaven. Dad knew how much Mum loved Smokey-the-cat, so Dad thought he'd make Mum a nice Christmas present by making a mat out of Smokey. Dad knows how to make a mat out of a cat because in the days when everyone was poor, Dad camped out in the bush to catch possums and sold their skins for two pounds a dozen. I never saw Smokey-the-cat nailed out on the workbench in the car shed but my big sister Robyn did, and Robyn cried so hard Dad dug up Smokey-the-cat without skin and buried Smokey-the-cat again with skin. But Mum still won't talk to Dad for days.

'Come on,' says Dad, picking up my new second-hand red bike. 'Let's go outside and get a photo.'

'That's a good bike, that is!' I heard Dad tell Mum when he came home from the dump. 'A coat of paint, it'll be as good as new.'

We head outside. Betty says, 'Don't carry your dolly by the hair!' Dad says, 'Now, sit down here, beside your sisters.' Robyn says, 'Take it without her if she wants to sulk.' Dad says, 'The crotons will make a nice background.' Mum says, 'Come on, sweetheart, smile for Daddy.' Dad says, 'Don't squint, eyes open wide.' It's hard smiling when you're looking straight into the sun and you got a second-hand bike and a plastic doll for Christmas.

I think for a bit I might run away but where would I go? Where would I live? What would I eat? How do you to boil a negg? How do you *buy* a negg? I got three pennies in my piggy bank but just how much does one negg cost? And what do you say to the man behind the counter? *Can I have one negg please and how much does one negg cost?* And what if the man behind the counter laughs at me? Or what if the man behind the counter is a bad man and comes out from behind his counter? It's no good—I'm gonna have to live forever with my mum and dad even if they're still not talking.

'Sweetheart,' says Mum, 'Santa knows we've got no room for a pony.'

I say, 'But Grandma's got lots of room for lots of ponies, you could ask Grandma ...'

Another year is a very long time to wait for Santa and my pony. A year is a long time when you're five and you didn't start school this year because you'll be six in March *next* year and it's better if you're a little older to start school next year. My sisters look forward to school holidays. I don't. On the last Friday of school term, I watch Robyn and Betty climb into the back of Granny Chapman's old grey Land Rover. I watch them climb over cousins' legs and boxes of Granny's grocery shop and squat on Granny's big bags of corn and flour. Mum and me wave goodbye and Granny's Land Rover heads off down the road in a grey cloud of cracker dust and a chorus of loud voices: *Jingle bells, jingle bells, jingle all the way.* All the kids sing all the way out to Fletcherview; only I'm not allowed to go out to Fletcherview because Granny doesn't want little kids under her feet. I only get to go to Grandma's on Christmas Day.

'Lucky!' I yell. 'Mum, can Lucky come to Grandma's?'

'No, sweetie. You know Grandma has two big cattle dogs, and they might not like Lucky. Run and get your dolly now so we can get going.'

'Mum … Can't you *please* ask Grandma about my pony? You had a pony when you were little. And even Dad had a pony!'

No one's listening, so I get in the car and sulk.

But then I can't help thinking about Dad's poor pony. First time I heard Toby's story was one time we went camping. We were all sitting round the fire, and Dad was telling stories about when he was little. But the saddest story was about his little pony.

*

Mount Hogan: December 1924

Usually of a morning, Fred would lie quiet until he heard the creak of bedsprings, then a sneeze as his mum poked at the embers of last night's fire, until he saw a match strike and flare orange in cupped hands as his dad coaxed a flannel wick into flame. Fred and his dad had made those lamps. All you needed was an empty jam tin filled with fat—*just like that, see, not too full, but.* Fred had held the flannel strips his mum had cut—*Roll 'em real good an' tight, then set 'em in the fat, like that, see?*

Fred's dad made all sorts. 'Good as any store-bought broom that is,' old George had said, giving Fred's mum, Emily, a sapling bound with the small branches of a beefwood tree. 'Good as any store-bought stilts those are,' old George had said, giving Fred two saplings punched through the tops of big jam tins for Christmas.

Fred's dad was a good builder too: old George had built the first grocery store in Kidston, and two houses to rent to miners sick of living in tents. George had built their home from galvanised iron and tin—*An' we water an' crush ant bed for the floors. Crushed and watered ant bed sets hard as cement, see?*

Fred had learned most everything he knew from his dad. What, with the nearest school forty mile away at Kidston, Fred only had 'proper lessons' twice a year. Last time the travelling teacher came trundling down the bush track in his buggy, Fred had learned 'Australia's rich from growing wool for uniforms during the war to end all wars'. According to that teacher, Australia was 'still riding high on the back of a sheep!' but Fred had figured out for himself that the Bagnalls didn't have no sheep, not to be ridin' on anywhere.

'Best be on the road afore sun up,' old George had yawned last night. 'Big day tomorra.'

Fred threw out a hand, but his brother Bert's side of the mattress was empty. With Bert turned fifteen—and sisters Florrie and May grown and gone—*That makes you me liddle afterthought, doan it, Freddie?*

Feeling in the dark, Fred found his pants, rolled back onto his shoulders, kicked his feet into the air and pulled his trousers on.

He felt for his shirt, pulled it on and did the buttons with hasty fingers. It was a long way to Pentland, where George had bought a little house on the main street, near the tennis courts, not far from Charters Towers.

This morning there'd be no going to the mine for old George, no sweeping ant-bed floors with beefwood brooms for Emily, no panning for specks of gold in nearby gullies for Fred—*Dip, an' swirl the water round and round real fast, see? Discard the top dirt, dip and swirl, and discard again, see?* The Bagnalls were moving to Pentland: three hotels, a butcher shop, a post office, a grocery store, a railhead, *and other kids for yer to go t'school with, Freddie.*

His mum and dad still sleeping, Fred tiptoed to the safe and sneaked a handful of sugar lumps. Toby's sugar lumps in one pocket, and Granddad-with-one-hand's bag of marbles—*Merry Christmas, Freddie*—in the other, Fred slipped outside before Emily could tell him, *Here ya go, Fred, you hold these toasting forks, an' don't let the bread git too close an' burn, 'cause it's the last bread we got fer now.*

The sun had yet to rise but the moon was smiling thinly: world ash grey, coaches sketched in charcoal. Just about everything they owned was loaded on those coaches; even Fred's new boots—*We'll keep 'em fer good, mind!*—were in that big rusted trunk on Dad's coach. Fred's stilts weren't loaded; those stilts had worked real good all of Christmas Day, but the next day the jam tins kept falling off the saplings. *George'll make ya some new stilts, when we git to Pentland. Maybe take three weeks to git to Pentland, but we'll be callin' at stations all along the way: Oak Park, Pandanus, Wandovale, Cargoon and Lolworth …*

The names of faraway places conjured a certain wonder in young Fred's mind, and Pentland was ever so much bigger than Mount Hogan. When the Bagnalls waved goodbye today, they'd be waving goodbye only to old Charlie Withers and his shanty at Mount Hogan.

Fred had already imagined The Arrival. There would be his dad driving the draught horses in the big coach: *Mareeba – Mount Molloy – Mount Carbine Mail Run* painted on one side, and *George Bagnall Proprietor* on the other. There'd be Emily driving the buggy horses, Nellie and Smarts, in the small coach, and Bert riding his horse, Spinner, and then there'd be Fred, riding Toby in the lead— and wearing his new boots. Whole town'd probably come out and watch the Bagnalls come to Pentland.

Fred ran down to the creek. At the sliprails, he listened for the sound of the horse bell, and heard it running, *tinker-tinker-tink-tink-tink*, through the grey trees over yonder. Bert wasn't far away, so Fred climbed through the sapling rails that guarded the well in the corner—he didn't want to be in the way when Bert and Toby brought the carriage horses cantering across the sandy creek bed. Waiting, he peered down into the black hole of the well, but it was still too dark to see the water down there. George called it a well; Emily called it *a darned cylinder stuck in sand*. His dad had sunk the iron cylinder upright into the sandy bank. Before the first flood each year, George bolted a steel lid down on top; after the flood, you only had to shovel sand off the lid to have clean water again. But whether you called it a *well* or a *darned cylinder stuck in sand*, it was still 200 yards from the house, and the water just as heavy.

Tinker-tinker-tink-tink-tink! Grey ghosts flitting among charcoal trees became horses cantering across the creek and up into the yard.

Bert slipped off Toby and slipped the slip rails home. 'Come an' git some breakfast first,' he said, taking Toby's bridle off. 'I'll help ya saddle 'im later.'

Bert ran on up to the house, but Fred had to *give Toby his sugar lumps!*

Toby was nuzzling Fred's hand when the big horses came shouldering in, jostling jealously. Big Bessie, ears flat and teeth bared, lunged; Toby wheeled away, and suddenly Fred was on his hands and knees in the midst of trampling hooves, snaking heads and horses squealing.

The surge of milling animals snapped a sliprail. Toby kicked up; Big Bessie hit Toby on the flank, spinning Toby like a top against the guard rail. Coach horses jumped the bottom sliprail, and galloped away. On hands and knees, Fred stared at the top half of Toby; bottom half of Toby was being swallowed by the well.

Improbable world: silence, backdrop grey.

Toby's splayed legs held him on the rim, but Toby's hooves were scoring the ground as his weight dragged him down, one slow inch at a time.

Fred whimpered; Toby grunted. Fred wailed, 'Dad!' And the real world came back.

'Dad!' Fred was screaming up the slope for all he was worth: 'Daaaaad!'

George came running, pulling up suspenders; Bert outran him, dropped on his knees beside Toby, breathed, 'Jesus bloody Christ!', grabbed a halter from the fence, slipped it over Toby's head and leaned his weight against the rope.

Toby grunted. Bert cursed. George muttered, 'Jesus Christ Almighty!'

Toby struggled, straining. 'Whoa, whoa, there now, Toby, whoo now, boy!' Toby lurched, slipped down further and was wedged; neck thrown back against the cylinder, fetlocks hooked on the rim.

'Git outta the way, Fred!' George leaned on the halter rope with Bert. 'Run and git the long rope, Fred! Over in the coach! Go on, run!'

Bawling blind, Fred ran, got the rope, ran back, tripping and stumbling on trailing coils. Emily, in her nightshirt, leaned over Toby, whispered, 'Oh, Lord!'

The rope round Toby's neck was hitched to a post. George stood back. 'He won't go down no further now.'

Eyes rolling white, Toby's legs and shoulders were bleeding—grey hide peeled away in strips—and Toby's every breath was a long exhaled groan.

'Yer all standin' there, doin' nothin'!'

'Shut up, Fred! Gotta think it through!'

Toby struggled, and Toby slipped down further.

'One of the draughts'll pull 'im out!'

'They're gone! Could take half a day, to catch 'em, on foot!'

Toby gagged, his long pink tongue lolling, and the rope cut in tighter.

'Jaysus!'

Fred was stroking Toby's face, begging Toby to put his tongue back in, and everyone was praying: *Good Lord! Jesus Christ! Gawd all-bloody-mighty!*

'Come an' git on this rope, Emily. Git them rails, Bert. Git good strong ones!'

George rigged a tripod: it was sturdy, could hold Toby up all day, but there was just no way to take up Toby's weight.

'Feed the rope here, can ya git ya hand down there? What if … ? Can ya … ?'

At once, Dad and Bert and Emily fell silent; the only sound was Fred crying.

'Take Fred back to the house,' George told Emily.

Fred was struggling, kicking at his mum. Emily wrapped him tightly in her arms and dragged him up the slope and back into the house. 'Look at you!' Emily said much too loudly, 'With yer pants on back t'front, and yer shirt all crossed-buttoned.'

She pulled him close, held his head against her chest, but Fred still heard the shot.

Through the window, against a sky bleeding streaks of red and gold, Fred saw a silhouette climb onto the coach, rummage about. Bert came inside, said nothing, wouldn't look at Fred, took the biggest butcher knife from a packing case, thought about it, took out two smaller knives as well. Outside, the silhouette had an axe in one hand, a saw in the other.

Two long, man-shaped shadows snaked their way back down towards the well: Fred's dad and Bert, heading down the slope to get Toby out of that darned cylinder stuck in sand.

3

A mother lost, lost hers ...

Christmas 2012

Morning comes, as mornings do.

There'll be no smells of roasting turkey, no voices raised in protest, no glasses raised in toast.

I'm at the bookcase. On the top shelf, diminutive spiders spin yarn for sepia eyes in frames: *Mum and Dad, sunlight on confetti ... Granny Chapman ... my sister, swimming with dolphins ...* the stories that I tell myself about my life.

I've already scanned the higher shelves; now, on hands and knees, in growing agitation, I run a finger along the last row of spines ...

Have I lost it? Thrown it out?

Eureka! I pluck a little paperback from between weightier neighbours, sink back on my heels. *North Queensland Cavalcade: a history of Charters Towers and other stories.* Brush a cobweb from the cover, thumb-flick the pages. Somewhere, tucked between my father's carefully researched facts and figures, is a little bush yarn about a boy whose pony fell down a well: a memory that survives in keystrokes, black on white.

He saw the world in black and white—right and wrong—my father. He came from a time when a man was only as good as his word, a time when *truth* wasn't negotiable or *loyalty* a commodity to be traded.

I put his book aside, and return instead to my mother's scrapbook: fading memories of people who no longer exist; captions scrawled in my mother's generous hand: *The Valley of Lagoons is among my happiest memories. Definitely the happiest time of my childhood ...*

Perhaps we all remember something of the gloss and glamour of our childhoods, and not the daily grind, but, for all their broken continuities and diffractions, the memories are no less real.

I wonder about those internal dialogues of a young girl—the things she told herself about the people she loved and the events that shaped the woman and the mother she became. Here's a photo of Big Minnie and Skinny Minnie, two elderly Aboriginal women in hand-me-down dresses braving posterity with uncertain smiles; another one of Frankie Gertz, an unexpected black baby delivered in the kitchens and dressed in the white smock taken from a little porcelain doll with broken toes ...

And here's my grandmother, glaring at the world with grim determination.

Time and distance can't diminish Granny Chapman.

Time and space can't erase the remembered scents and sounds of celebrations past.

*

Fletcherview: Christmas 1964

There are two types of people in the world: bushies and townies. My mum's a townie now, but Ollie Bagnall used to be a bushie when she was Olive May Chapman.

When first I heard my Granny Chapman owned thirty square mile of country, I thought Granny must own half the world. But my mum says Fletcherview is only little compared to other cattle stations. Mum says Granny had to sell off bits and pieces when things started to go wrong. Mum was only a young girl when *things started to go wrong* but she still gets a bit sad when I ask about my granddad Dick. My mum's got a little piece of Granddad Dick's shinbone; she keeps it in a tiny glass bottle in her underwear drawer.

Fletcherview is only seventeen mile out of town but it takes more than half an hour to get there. It's a long, hot trip on a winding red-dirt road when you're feeling sick, squashed up between two big sisters, with a Bowen Special mango on your lap. Every Christmas Mum gives Granny a cement pot for ferns on her veranda, but my dad's been giving my granny a special mango every Christmas since 1946. This time Dad couldn't buy a special mango in the shops because the wind blew the blossom off the trees, so we couldn't leave town until Dad found a special mango, and Dad drove round and round and round town until I got sick when Dad stopped at a tree had fruit hanging over the fence. I hate being late. I like to be at Granny's and watch for the other cars coming along the red-dirt road.

We cross Little Sandy Bridge; you know you're *nearly* there when you cross Big Sandy Bridge. As our little Volksie bumps up the rocky jump-up, I sit up straighter because all this is Granny Chapman's country now. There are big black basalt rocks on both sides of the road, and in the paddocks you can see Grandma's white-faced Herefords branded 3VB.

It was right here on this road my mum waved to my dad. When Granny was driving into town on Fridays to do the weekly shop, my dad was chopping wood for the council right here on Granny's road. Mum used to go to town with Granny, and it makes me feel good thinking of Dad waiting for the Land Rover every Friday morning, just so he could wave to his sweetheart. I close my eyes and I can see him … but the car moves on, and in a flash that young man has gone.

After the jump-up you can see Granny's house ahead. It used to have a veranda running right around the second floor too, but they closed in the top veranda with corrugated tin to make more rooms because in the olden days Granny's house at Fletcherview was a wayside inn for buggies travelling into Charters Towers from other stations further up the road.

There are three cars parked out the front of Granny's ugly house, so we're the last to arrive. We rattle across a new cattle grid. Last year there was a gate you had to stop and open. Dad turns into the drive and parks beside the other cars under the athel trees, and Granny's two big red dogs come barking down the dog-yard fence. At Granny's place there are three yards. The dog yard goes all the way round the back to the fuel and machinery sheds; on the other side of Granny's house is a big chook run and orange trees.

Granny and my aunties and cousins are all waiting under the Christmas trees—Granny calls those trees crepe myrtles, but us kids call them Christmas trees because they get their flowers just in time for Christmas.

'Hello! Hello!' They all come crowding through the gate. 'And how've ya been keepin'?'

Dad gives Granny that damned mango made us late.

Granny doesn't even come up to my dad's shoulder. Granny is short but Granny is big. Granny's not soft big, but sort of hard big. Mum's got a photo of Granny with her hair down past her waist but Granny's got short dark-grey hair now and she pulls it straight back from her face with bobby pins. Granny's skin on her big arms is like when you put a sheet of paper over a fire and it turns brown and buckles. And Granny's really mean—got a mouth turned down at both ends, and eyes in the back of her head.

The grown-ups are all hugging and kissing. The kids are showing off presents so I run over to the dog-yard fence. Rover is a cranky old dog and ol' Sal's only got one good eye, but they stand on their hind legs and paw at the fence with their tongues all hanging out. Granny never has trouble selling red rover puppies but Granny's kept one puppy this year. I'm just trying to push my hand through the mesh to pat the puppy when: 'You!' Granny shouts. 'Git away from there! I don't want you kids messin' with that pup!'

Everyone is looking at me. I run back to Mum's hand. Even Aunty June—where I got my name Pamela June—is feeling sorry for me. She messes up my hair and says, 'Look how much you've grown!'

I smile at my cousin Jackie and pretend I don't care Granny roused at me. Jackie shows me her new gold bangle and I tell Jackie, 'I got a new second-hand red bike with pink tassels Dad can't fit in the car so I can't show you.'

Uncle Owen says he's going to take David and Richard out on the flat to try out David's new cricket bat and ball. David's telling Richie how Don Bradman's the greatest batsman of all time, average: 99.94, and David says us girls can't play because it's a real cricket ball and we're too little and *you'd just get in the way!*

Aunty Melva gives Jan a push. 'Go and show Pam and Jackie your new farm set.'

'Wanna play?' Jan says, holding out her new farm set.

First time I met Jan was when Dad drove us out to Weinbah on the flat downs country round Julia Creek. Jan had riding pants and cowboy boots and a black straw cowboy hat, and brown hair cut short like boy hair. I said, 'You're pretty,' and Jan said, 'You're stupid!' Then Jan disappeared back down the dam bank, yelling, 'Ya just a stupid townie!'

'Wanna play?' Jan says today, showing me her new farm set.

I leave Jackie because Jackie's a stupid townie, and run off with

Jan because Jan lives on a sheep station and Jan has a Whopper Farm set and not a silly gold bangle. Jan and me run across the cement veranda and I stop and look at the big cracks and some of the cement lifted so high you can stick your fingers underneath. I stick my fingers underneath and Jan tells how the big flood caused them cracks when the water went right up to the roof of Granny's ugly house and now the cement is ugly too. Standing on my tiptoes I can't reach the second-storey floor, so it doesn't seem true that the water went right up to the roof.

I squat down with Jan in the dirt beneath the big old pine tree beside Granny's big chook yard and I tell Jan, 'I got a new second-hand bike two weeks before Christmas so Mum and Dad can see if I can reach the pedals and so Dad can make it as good as new with a coat of red paint, and Mum bought a new set of pink plastic tassels for the handlebars so I can ride to school with Betty because Robyn goes to the high school now and Dad can't fit my new red bike in the car so I can't show you.'

But Jan says how she got a new gold Go-Go bike with gold tassels for us to ride to school together when they sell their sheep station, and Jan's Go-Go bike has gears and Jan got a Whopper Farm for Christmas with more than fifty pieces.

I wave at Robyn and my cousin Jennifer going through the gate into the chook yard. The chook yard's as big as the house yard and right over there is the henhouse and laying boxes and roosts. The chook yard's got four orange trees, two mandarins and a lemon tree, and right alongside this fence is a big wire cage Robyn and Jennifer go in and cut bunches of Granny's purple grapes.

When we set up Jan's farm, we decide to crack some nuts. Granny's nuts come with shells on. Almonds are easy: mostly, you can crack almonds with your teeth but you need one of Granny's hammers for the Brazil nuts, walnuts and monkey nuts.

'You kids crack them nuts outside!'

We go out to the side veranda and find a good small crack in the cement. The big cracks caused by the big flood are no good 'cause your nut falls right in and you got to get one of Granny's screw-drivers to lever it out, but little cracks are very handy for putting your nut in so it won't skid away when you hit it with Granny's hammer.

Dad and Uncle Jack are out on this side of the veranda talking with Uncle Ian about how the country is being run, and how everyone's got everything nowadays, and how no one had anything in the days when everyone was poor.

Uncle Ian's got sticky-out eyebrows and little sandy hairs coming out his ears and nose. Uncle Ian's my aunty Dulcie's second husband. Aunty Dulcie's first husband was killed right here on Fletcherview, just out there, right outside the chook yard where Uncle Owen is bowling balls to Don Bradman and Richie. Aunty Dulcie's first husband was Bill Whalen. One day, they were mustering cattle up into the cattle yards up there and my Aunty June had a new horse called Actress who was acting up. So, even though my Uncle Bill had a broken arm and a plaster cast on his arm, Uncle Bill got on Actress to straighten her out for Aunty June, but Actress played up some more and fell right over the top of a big cow and that's how come Aunty Dulcie's married to Uncle Ian now.

Uncle Ian's really clever, but a year or two back Uncle Ian had some troubles so my Dad and Granny Chapman had to go a long way down south to pick up Alison and Richard and they lived with us *just for a little bit so Uncle Ian can sort out his troubles without his kids to worry about.* One night Robyn was doing the washing-up and Alison and Betty were drying, and Alison and Betty kept sneaking up behind Robyn and pinching her on her bum. It was really fun, so I sneaked up too, but just when Robyn had had enough, so when I pinched Robyn on her bum, Robyn didn't know it was me and Robyn kicked a tooth down my throat so Mum and Dad had to rush me to hospital and good ol' Doc Ellis fished my tooth out of my neck before I choked to death and nearly died.

We hear the cow bell ring. 'Come on, you girls!'

Granny's dining room is like party land. The big kids decorated it, and there's a big she-oak in a sand bucket. Wish I was here when the big kids got the tree, but I'm glad I wasn't here when they ran down two of Granny's turkeys and Granny chopped their heads off.

Like I told, Fletcherview used to be a hotel in the olden days, so there's a really big redwood table in the dining room. There are twenty-two of us and Granny makes twenty-three, but we fit at the big table because Aunty Dulcie tells Tony and John they have to sit at the little kids' table Granny set up in the corner. Granny's organising everyone with her carving knife: 'You sit there, Dulce, an' Geoffrey in the high chair. Melva and Owen over there, an' Ollie and Fred here, an' June and Jack … You kids keep it down!' The kids are all so loud Granny can't even hear herself think. 'All you big kids git up the other end. Go on, git!'

Geoffrey's bawlin' he *don't wanna sit in the high chair* and Betty's squabbling with Alison and Judith about who gets to sit at the bottom of the table. 'All three of ya can fit there! Push ya chairs in closer.' Jan's little sister is swinging from Aunty Melva's apron. 'Just wait till I finish servin', Gail, an' ya can sit on me lap,' Aunty Melva says. And Geoffrey's still squawking he *don't wanna sit in the high chair!*

Uncle Owen comes in carrying one big turkey Granny chopped the head off of on Granny's silver platter—'Merry Christmas!'—and pretends like he cooked that turkey all by his own just like he pretended last year. Wish my dad was like Uncle Owen. Uncle Owen's got the widest mouth and biggest smile and when something goes wrong, Uncle Owen says, *Well, ya can't help bad luck, can ya?* and throws back his head and laughs. Or, *Ya don't know ya elbow from ya arsehole!* And when my uncle Owen laughs you can't help but laugh with him. (They say my uncle Owen might've been tickled by a tarbrush, so maybe that's why Uncle Owen's always laughing?)

Aunty Melva shifts the leg of pork, Mum shuffles the roast pumpkin and potatoes, and Granny finds a clear spot for a big ham baked with breadcrumbs. 'Ollie, you can carve the ham.' Granny runs her hands down the bib of her apron, pushes her glasses up on her big nose and looks about to see what's missing. All along Granny's big redwood table are china bowls of nectarines, plums and peaches and plates of dried fruits and sugared nuts.

'Git outta them chocolates, you boys, they're fer afters. Didya hear me, Richie?'

Granny's big knife flashes against her sharpening steel. 'Give the boys a drumstick,' Granny says. (Granny doesn't know us girls'd like a drumstick too!)

Crackers go bang and party poppers pop and streamers of crepe paper hit the big wooden beams and dangle from the decorations. Geoffrey's still bawling he's *not gonna sit in the high chair!* and before too long Uncle Jack can't hear himself think, and he stands up and leaves Granny's big redwood table. Jackie looks like she might cry, and I tell Jackie, 'I'll help you pull your cracker if you like; I'm not scared.'

Aunty Dulcie's thinking she might take Geoffrey upstairs and put him down. I'm thinking, 'bout time too! But I know there's not a family in Australia—in all the world—as happy or as lucky as Granny Chapman's clan.

After dinner, the grown-ups have a lie down, or play chess or cards, but we go and play on Granny's buggy. Granny's old buggy is parked under some trees between Granny's turkey run and pigpens. Granny used to live at Fletcherview when she was little but then she married Granddad Dick and went to live on other stations and work for a bigwig, name of James Simpson Love, but when Mr Love died he made my granddad boss of all his properties and that's how come they got enough money to drive Granny's buggy all the way to Fletcherview, a home of their own.

Granny doesn't drive her buggy nowadays, just us kids do.

Richard and David got cap guns for Christmas, and us girls didn't, so us girls are the Indians, the Mexicans or the horses. Down Mexico way there are bad Mexicans wanted for murders hiding in the turkey yard, and thievin'-low-life Injuns hiding in the pigpens. The bad Mexicans wanted for murders wear big hats and have no teeth—only sometimes black ones—and the thieving Injuns are always looking to scalp the men trying to settle in the west in our wagon train. We always play America. Who'd wanna be Ned Kelly with a bucket on your head when you can be no-count-low-life-thievin' redskins riding paint-coloured ponies with sapling bows and arrows, whooping and doing war dances with Granny's turkey feathers stuck in your hair?

After a bit, David circles the wagons and puts the brake against the wheel, and us girls climb in Granny's buggy, but David makes a rude noise, and Richie jumps down, making rude noises under his armpit—'Fart! Fart!'—and laughing real loud.

I say, 'You shouldn't say that word!'

Jan looks at me funny and says, 'What should they say?'

'They should say *let off* or *blow off*. And they shouldn't do it anyway!'

Jan says, 'Aw, grow up, would'ja!'

I don't like Jan telling me *Aw, grow up would'ja* so I start telling how I asked Santa to bring me a piebald pony like Tonto rides or maybe like the Cisco Kid's horse, Diablo.

Jan giggles. 'Santa?'

'Santa?' Alison looks at me funny. 'Santa!' Then Jan and Alison laugh like I said something real funny or like maybe Santa is the funniest joke in the world. They jump down from the buggy and race after the boys yelling, 'Guess who believes in Santa! Guess who believes in Santa!'

When I tell Mum what they said, Mum says, 'Santa only comes to little girls who believe in him.' And I tell Mum, 'I'm always gonna believe in Santa.' Then I ask Mum why's Granny so mean, but Mum says, 'Grandma's not really mean, sweetheart, it's just that old people sometimes get a little bit crotchety.'

*

Fletcherview: January 1942

Late one afternoon in January '42, May Chapman set the buggy brake, and took a moment to look up at the double-storey house. Formerly Fletcherview Coach Inn—a favourite watering hole for daytrippers coming out from Charters Towers to enjoy picnics at the Big Rocks—the house was about to become 'Fletcherview Homestead'.

In truth, the house had nothing of the stately elegance of the homesteads at the Valley of Lagoons or Gainsford Station, and nothing of the water views afforded by the properties of the J.S. Love Estate. There was no waterlilied lake, and no river view at Fletcherview.

The name 'Fletcherview' was doubly misleading: early settlers coming across Lolworth Creek thought they'd stumbled on the Fletcher, some thirteen mile north. Once, the two creeks had been one river—running from the Great Dividing Range into the Burdekin—but a volcano near the headwaters had filled the original river, bank to bank, with molten lava. When the rains came again, new watercourses had formed along each side of the lava flow; the northern stream became the Fletcher, and the southern one, Lolworth Creek.

No matter. May Chapman had come home.

And, for just a moment, May was little May Wheeler again: the little goat girl from Begorra Waterhole who milked her goats and took the milk on her Shetland pony cart to the Charters Towers hospital; the little girl whose parents had scraped together the pounds to buy the roadside inn at Fletcherview—a home of their own. *Look after the pennies, May; the pounds will look after themselves ...*

It was the fourth time the Chapmans had made the thirteen-mile trek from Gainsford Station down to Fletcherview in as many days. On this, the last trip, Olive and little Melva had ridden beside May on the buggy—a buggy piled high with potted plants and kerosene tins sprouting citrus trees; fowl coops, two poddy lambs and a poddy calf, and their surrogate mother—an old milk goat called Barbara. Melva had spent the journey sulking; her petulant cry—*I wanna ride with Daddy and his boys!*—only silenced when May had threatened to put her in the coop to ride along with the turkey gobbler.

Melva had jumped from the buggy and was doing somersaults on the front lawn; Olive was lifting Barbara and her babies down. In her mind's eye, May was *planting crepe myrtles along the front fence, and two big book-leaf pines, one there and one there, at either corner of the house.* The fowl run, where rosella bushes were running wild, *blossomed into an orchard: orange trees, mandarins, grapes, and one lemon tree, for cooking.* As May's mother used to say, 'You can't plant lemons and expect to harvest oranges, May.'

May was *hoeing a vegie patch beside the fowl run* when ...

'They're coming!'

On the north-western slopes, etched against a lowering sun, Dick and his two 'boys', Dulcie and June, were turning a herd of goats up towards the stock yards. There'd be no Aboriginal stockmen, just Dick and his two 'boys' to run the property; there'd be no Aboriginal maids, cooks, washerwomen or gardeners either, just May and Ollie to run the house. No matter.

May Chapman had come home.

Fletcherview was only thirty square mile of country, but with Lolworth beyond the homestead, Pandanus to the west, Big Sandy and Little Sandy creeks to the south, and the Burdekin River as the north-eastern boundary, Fletcherview had the potential, as Dick had said, 'to be the best little cattle station in the district'.

The Burdekin drained an area of 50,500 square mile of country and, apart from the Murray, was economically the most important river in Australia. On paper, most of the Burdekin basin would appear to be ideal for crops, but the rainfall was so erratic the country was only suitable for low-density grazing. On its 450-mile journey, the Burdekin was more than half a mile wide in places, but, on Fletcherview—in the Chapmans' backyard—the mighty river passed through a narrow gorge only twenty feet wide in places. The Big Rocks—massive beds of river-smooth pink rock and whirlpool-hollowed caves—was a magical place for swimming and fishing and messing about in boats. There were miles of sandy banks and dunes and, hidden by a towering wall of black basalt, a deep switchback called the Dead Hole. Lower down, the Little Rocks' layered beds of grey shale stone were a treasure trove of fossilised coral and mysterious little prehistoric creatures. *All in good time*, the Chapmans would have time for picnics at the Big and Little Rocks …

But for now, Olive was feeding Barbara; Barbara was feeding her orphaned babies. Melva had run off to help Daddy and his boys but May was inspecting her old new home—the place where she had spent so many happy years as a young girl. In the dining room, she ran a hand along the redwood dining table and could almost hear the echo of voices past—or the murmur of voices future?

The kitchen was set apart, built separate for risk of fire. Little flecks of late sun peeping through old nail holes speckled the sapling supports and soot-blackened tin. There was an old wood stove in one corner; beside it, a wood box built into the wall. Tomorrow, May would *kill and roast a turkey, make butter, damper and rosella jam for smoko*. Tonight, they'd make do on cold corned meat and boiled potatoes.

Beyond the kitchen was a butcher shed, and in the dog yard a four-bay machinery shed made from hand-hewn timber and corrugated tin. The Plymouth had already taken up residence, but when the 'powers that be' started rationing petrol—if it came to that—the buggy would come back into its own. Australia was at war.

Supposing, planning, May made her way around to the front of the house. Fourteen years ago, in '27, a one-in-a-hundred-year flood had risen into the floorboards of the second storey. *All in good time*, Dick would *move the house onto higher ground*, up there to the south-west.

May gave a little start. Dick had stolen up behind her. He wrapped his arms around her; she leaned back into the embrace. 'You were right, May,' Dick told her. 'We're going to make a good life here.'

*

Christmas 2012

My mother's memories …

It's growing late when I turn a page of her scrapbook and am arrested by a page of typed text:

My mother was never happy on the other stations—as my father was practically a stranger to us. Mum always wanted to go back to Fletcherview. You would expect that a woman with

47

four daughters to rear and a large overdraft would give up, but my mother set out to run the station with one stockman, Bill Whalen—who married Dulcie and was killed a short time later.

To me, Fletcherview became a place of tragedies and, for a long time, I couldn't face writing about it ... I get no pleasure from going to Fletcherview anymore.

I didn't know my mother felt that way about Fletcherview. I should have known.

4

The Widow Maker

New Year 2013

The world is full of tragedies—without you needing to go looking for them: starving refugees, suicide bombers, school shootings, crazed gunmen, beheadings that send shock waves around the world. Shake your own head—still attached—turn the page: *Bus Tragedy … Boat Tragedy … Bridge Tragedy …*

In a world of BIG DEATHS IN BOLD HEADLINES, my 'little deaths' scarcely rate a mention. You don't care. Why should you? People die; that's what people do.

Mothers die—and sometimes fathers kill them—leaving the orphaned child trying to make sense of it all by googling 'Grief—dealing with the loss of a parent'; trying to reconstruct a sense of self by revisiting the past: a time when each new year brought with it the suspended expectation of so much more to come.

*

Fletcherview: New Year 1967

Granny Chapman is a widow.

Granny was made a widow by a Widow Maker. A Widow Maker is a very bad man hangs around Fletcherview late at night. You can't see him in the dark because he wears a long black robe; only sometimes you might catch a glimpse of his bony fingers, or see some moonlight flashing on his scythe. The big black hat covers half his grinning, death-skull face, and this is just as well because if a Widow Maker ever doffs his hat to you, you must *never* look into his eyes: those hollow eyes can suck you inside out, and then, if you've been good, you get sent right off up to heaven, but if you've been bad you become a Widow Maker too.

A Widow Maker sucked my granddad in, and spat him straight on up to heaven.

When the old homestead comes in sight, I get butterflies in my tummy thinking of the Widow Maker because since the school holidays started I've been getting under Mum's feet.

'Get out from under me feet, love, can't you see I'm busy?'

'Can't I stay at Granny's with all the big kids, Mum, just for one night? Please!'

'We'll see.'

We'll see means you've got a fifty-fifty chance, and I really want to stay at Granny's for New Year because the big kids have built a big bonfire out in the cattle lane and Granny's bought boxes of fireworks and bungers and little crackers. On New Year, Granny lets the kids stay up and play musical chairs and winks—or sometimes the kids hold hands and walk around the veranda in the dark singing, 'Moonlight, starlight, the Boogie won't come out tonight', and get themselves all wound up and scared half to death, then at midnight the kids go out into the lane and light the big bonfire and let the fire crackers off.

Jan is clinging to the front fence. I'm ever so jealous because Jan's mum and dad live at Fletcherview now. Aunty Melva is Granny's cook, and Uncle Owen—*Ya can't help bad luck, can ya?*—is head stockman. The minute the car pulls up I jump out and run over to the gate.

'Come on!' Jan says. 'I got somethin' to show ya.'

Under one of the Christmas trees is a baby calf—a pure white baby calf—and Jan's got a family-size Coke bottle of milk. I've never seen a snowy white calf before but he's really sick, this little calf: he's got big gashes down his legs and flies crawling about on the poop stuck on his bum and on his tail. He doesn't even lift his head when we squat down beside him he's hurt so bad. 'What happened to him?' I whisper.

'Dingoes got 'im,' Jan says. Then Jan tells how they were havin' dinner last night an' a car pulled off the road, an' a man come over to the gate an' hollered, an' they all ran out to the gate, an' the man told Uncle Owen and Granny how a pack of bloody mongrel dingoes was gettin' at them cows—just on the rise up there—and how Uncle Owen ran upstairs and got the rifle Granny keeps beside her bed because it was closer than the rifle up the shed, and how Jan and her dad and David drove up in Granny's Rover, but the dingoes heard 'em coming so her dad didn't even get a shot, an' those dogs had pulled down three calves, and Uncle Owen said it was too late for the other two calves, an' he shot 'em. Jan draws a breath. 'Dad reckons it's too late for this little fella too,' she says, but she won't let her dad shoot this calf because this calf isn't chewed up bad like the two little calves the dingoes got.

'I can sit 'im up,' Jan says, 'an' you help hold 'im.'

We roll Snowflake so he's against my knees and Jan lifts his head and puts her fingers between his little white teeth to open his mouth and puts the teat in. I wish my dad would rescue calves from dingoes and bring me home a white poddy calf, and it wouldn't even matter if it wasn't white. I got a pogo stick and a pair of ballet shoes for Christmas.

We try and try but Snowflake won't suck the teat. Jan's really disappointed 'cause he took a little bit this mornin'. We try dripping milk on Snowflake's tongue but Snowflake is too tired; Snowflake just wants to lie his head down onto the lawn.

Please, God! Please!

I'm still praying when Jan puts Snowflake's head down, sits back on her heels and says, 'He's not gonna make it.'

'We've gotta keep on tryin'!'

'Nah.' Jan wipes milky hands on her trousers. 'We oughta get Dad to put 'im down.'

I stand and I brush my hands on my shorts. 'No!'

Jan gives me a bushie look. 'He's not going to make it, ya know?'

'He might.'

'Look!' Jan says. 'Here come the Grahams, an' the Hamiltons behind 'em.'

Hello, hello, an' how 'ave ya been keepin'?

Everyone's going for a swim down in Lolworth Creek. 'You kids stay on the cattle pads!' All the aunties and the cousins are coming. 'Could be snakes in the long grass!' Only Granny's got to find a big stick to help her down the bank. And only Granny dabbles her toes in the water while us kids all duck-dive and try to bring sand up from the bottom, but no one can because Granny's pump hole is too deep.

After a quick dip, and a long, hot walk back again, I race Jan out to the front fence to sit with Snowflake under the Christmas tree but Snowflake's still very tired.

Granny rings the cowbell to let everyone know dinner's ready. Christmas decorations are still all up in Granny's dining room, only the she-oak in the corner is looking a bit sad.

Mum helps me pull my cracker and puts a green crown on my head. The dining room is so loud I can hardly hear myself think, but I find myself thinking about my granddad. Dick Chapman is looking down at me from up there on the wall. Granddad's wearing a work shirt and a brown hat. Granddad's green eyes have *bin touched up, 'cause the cameras weren't so good in them days* but Granddad Dick looks like a nice man and very handsome even with his eyes touched up.

Granddad Dick's dad came to Australia all the way from Ireland on a big sailing ship called *Merkara*, but Dick ran away from home when he was sixteen and worked on a cattle station for a man called Mr Morey. Granddad Dick was only twenty-two when Mr Morey made him head stockman of Valprai Station, and everyone who ever knew my granddad says, 'Dick Chapman was the best damned horse and cattleman I ever seen—both sides of the Burdekin.' That's why J.S. Love made Granddad Dick boss of all Mr Love's properties when Mr Love was dead and his estate was still sending horses to India for the British Indian Army as remounts and gunners.

Granny's peeling bits of rag off her plum pudding. 'Put the brandy sauce over there, June. Ollie, you do the custard and Melva can serve the ice-cream.'

Aunty Melva makes the best ice-cream in the world, and Aunty June is really pretty. One time I asked Dad how come Uncle Jack's mouth looks sort of sucked in like that, and Dad said Uncle Jack broke his false teeth and lost one half of his teeth so he only wears the other half of his teeth and that's why Uncle Jack's mouth looks sort of sucked in like that.

In World War II, Dad and Uncle Jack were in the army reserves but one day a man came along and said seeing as how there's no chance of their regiment being shipped to New Guinea anytime soon, did anyone want to volunteer for chopping wood for the city council for the boilers down at the Charters Towers weir? My dad and Uncle Jack said they wouldn't mind chopping wood, but Uncle Jack got tired of chopping wood and went back to Townsville, and the very next day the soldiers in Uncle Jack's unit were told they were being sent off to New Guinea. Uncle Jack thought he'd rather be chopping wood than fighting Nips in New Guinea so Uncle Jack ran away but the army caught him and put him in a cage and sent him to New Guinea anyway, so that's how come Uncle Jack got a medal says he was in New Guinea and my dad didn't get a medal for chopping wood. My dad's only got his slouch hat with one side pinned up with a Rising Sun badge.

Dad's brother, my uncle Bert, he didn't want to go to New Guinea either, so Uncle Bert ran away. But the army couldn't catch Uncle Bert and put him in a cage because Uncle Bert knows how to live on possums in the bush, and whenever he came to town, he hid behind the door at Grandma Emily's boarding house.

Granddad Dick didn't have to go to war, because he was growing cattle.

'Hope I get the secret sixpence in Granny's pudding again this year, Mum!'

'I think there might be a secret five cent in Grandma's pudding this year, love.'

With my green crown on my head, I look up at Granddad Dick, king of all horse and cattlemen. It all happened a very long time ago but I know my mum still misses her dad, and I suppose Granny must miss her husband too because Granny won't marry Joe Downey even if he asks her. There's a big wooden frame beside the first one. Granddad Dick is sitting in an old-fashioned wooden chair with his hands on his knees, and standing beside him is Granny in a lacy white wedding gown with lilies down to her knees—Granny wasn't so hard big in those days—and she's wearing funny pointy white shoes like boots. And, you know, I can't help but wonder if Dick Chapman might be unhappy living up there in heaven having New Year's dinner with God and Aunty Dulcie's first husband, my uncle Bill who fell over a cow with a broken arm. Granddad Dick's missing out on dinner with all his family—except Uncle Jack, who's sleeping in his car, but, most of all, I reckon Granddad Dick couldn't be happy, not with leaving Granny and his four girls to run a cattle station all by their own.

*

Fletcherview: 3 January 1944

New Year exploded above Fletcherview Homestead in a brief but spectacular display: violet-pink, indigo and blue-green pyrotechnic stars trailing silver horsetails across an infinite southern sky of stars. Fireworks, but no bonfire: *There's a war on, yer dozy gits! An' Breddon just a donkey fart down the road!*

During the last four years, almost a million US service personnel had visited Australian shores, and the Big Rocks—one of the most spectacular areas of the Burdekin River, *and right in our backyard!*— had become the chosen site for R and R of American servicemen stationed on the air-force base at Breddon. And, as everybody knew, American service men were *overpaid, over-sexed and over here!* May Chapman had been keeping a weather eye on her girls. She had cause for concern: more than 12,000 Australian women would become American war brides, most of whom would return to the US with their new husbands at the end of the war.

May Chapman wasn't taking any chances with blazing night fires and Jap planes either. She had, however, spent New Year's Eve with one eye on her girls tramping the paddocks around the homestead as they dragged logs and branches for their proposed bonfire in the cattle lane outside. And, when a passing jeep of American servicemen had stopped and the young men hanging from the sides had taken charge of bonfire building—'We'll give yer girls a hand, Mrs Chapman'—who was May to stop them?

For the latter part of the morning, May had kept one eye on her girls and one eye on the Yanks, who'd torn off shirts and flexed muscle on fallen trees and branches too big for her girls to drag or carry. May had even pointed out logs further afield that *might be snigged by yer jeep?* However, by the time the home paddocks had been cleared to May's satisfaction, and the last of the branches was being tossed high atop an impressive pile, May had both eyes firmly fixed on Olive, who was playing eye-tag with a young soldier called Johnny Marshal.

As the girls waved the boys on their way over to the Big Rocks, May pronounced herself well pleased: 'Good job, girls, we'll light it in the mornin',' and had silenced their protests: 'There's a war on, ya dozy gits! An' Breddon just a donkey fart down the road.'

So the new year at Fletcherview had been sung in on the back of 'Auld Lang Syne' and by a brief, but spectacular, fireworks display in the lane down beside the homestead.

If it wasn't for the Yanks camped in the Chapmans' backyard, May could almost have been forgiven for forgetting there was a war on at all. For all the Japs had dropped bombs on Australian soil— and three subs had entered Sydney Harbour—most times it seemed that the war was something happening *out there, over there, some-where far away.* True, bold black headlines had cried, 'The Battle of the Coral Sea', 'The Battle of the Kokoda Trail in New Guinea', and all of Australia had shuddered with the fall of Singapore, but the little ongoing inconveniences—rationing of clothes, meat and butter—had little or no effect on the Chapmans. The debacle faced by the government in trying to implement petrol rationing had finally resolved itself in petrol coupons, and, because the Yanks were a little leery of drinking river water, the Chapmans had given the US Army unlimited access to their water-storage tanks—*water pumped from Lolworth Creek, dozy gits!*—in exchange for petrol. May had fresh meat and poultry for barter, and butter was a favourite.

'Better make some more, Ollie. Them boys don't like that tin stuff the army feeds 'em.'

The illusion of a world at peace had been reinforced by the festival atmosphere on New Year's Day. The whole family had gone over to the Big Rocks; even Dick had taken the day off. From first light, the banks of the Burdekin had been cluttered with army trucks and jeeps and any number of civilian cars that had brought daytrippers out to picnic at the Rocks. There'd been tarpaulins strung between the paperbarks and tents rigged at the water's edge; a cricket match had been played out, Aussies versus Yanks, and a paddle regatta—Yanks paddling discarded belly tanks made into clumsy boats. There'd been fishing, swimming, card games, ball games, board games, battle games and, come lunchtime, the smell of piglets and turkeys roasting on open fires.

Olive had made a tidy profit. At dawn, she'd driven a heavily laden buggy across Lolworth Creek and parked it on the higher banks of the Burdekin River. Before smoko she'd been, 'Sorry, fellas, all sold out!' Gone were six turkeys (no ducks because the Red Cross had first dibs on her ducks), four weaner piglets and six dozen eggs, rosella and marmalade jam, and all her butter and three dozen pumpkin scones had disappeared, not having seen the true light of New Year's Day.

To a young girl not long turned sixteen, life was truly grand. A year back, after much begging and sulking, Olive had talked her dad into letting her leave St Gabes: 'Mum needs me to help run the house. It's all right for you, Dad, you've got Dulce and June and Melva.' Dick had secured an overdraft from the New South Wales Bank, and the Chapmans of Fletcherview now owned Marlow on Keelbottom and Southern View on Southern Cross Creek.

Plans to move the house to higher ground had been put on hold for another year.

On this, the third day of the new year, a clear dawn heralded by maggies was blossoming into another long, hot summer's day. A day as shiny and bright as a newly minted penny, Olive thought, must surely etch itself indelibly on the memory.

Dick was taking Majestic on his first ride, and June was riding Miss Maudie as chaperone for the mettlesome stallion. Old Miss Maudie, part draught and as gentle as the day was long, would keep Majestic calm. Dulce was taking Melva for a ride over to check the mill and troughs at Pandanus, and May was making scones for smoko. 'They'll all be back by smoko, Ollie, so put a wriggle in yerself!'

On the veranda, Olive stopped sweeping to watch her father and June riding down the lane. Majestic was a magnificent blood bay just rising three. Her dad had spent the last week mouthing, long-reining, bagging, sandbagging the young thoroughbred. He had *a good temperament*, but it was his first ride out and he was nervous, skittish. Rolling an eye back at Dick, Majestic was jiggling the bit and nipping at Miss Maudie.

Olive and her broom completed a circuit of the veranda. She was thinking of young Johnny Marshal asking her to write to him when he was shipped off to New Guinea, when something made her look up. Up there, in the distance, she saw movement; a moment later, the brown speck miraged into Majestic, running wild, reins trailing.

For one dreadful moment, Olive felt as though she was outside herself, watching herself watch another brown speck morph into June riding Maudie hell for leather back towards the homestead. 'Mum!' Olive cried. 'Muuum!'

There are certain kinds of cry any mother can interpret: unhappy cry, impatient cry, frightened cry. The *There's a big brown on the veranda!* cry, or *There's a pack of dingoes in the paddock!* cry. None of which can be confused with: *Mum! Muuum!*

May came running, saw Majestic—riderless—saw Maudie at full gallop, June urging the big mare on, regardless of rocky ground or gradient.

May clutched Olive's arm. In silence, mother and daughter ran to the gate.

May's heart felt empty but her head was full: *Take the buggy? No! Too slow … catch and hitch horses … the Plymouth?* May had never learned to drive—all in good time, Dick was going to teach her. The Plymouth was parked out front; Dick never left it parked out front but it was out there now. *There's a first-aid kit in the back …*

'Go git the key, Ollie!' May shook her arm free. 'Go on!'

Olive didn't move; she couldn't. Above the thunder of approaching hooves, they could hear June wailing now, and from the garbled sound, they plucked the words: 'It's Dad!'

June pulled Maudie to a halt; the mare was a sweaty lather, nostrils flared, flanks heaving, and the dust on June's red face was streaked by tears.

May grabbed the reins. June swung down, sagged in her mother's arms. 'It's Dad!'

'June!' May pushed her away, and shook her.

'It's Dad!' June cried, clutching at her mum. 'It's Dad!'

'Git the key, Ollie!' May shook June harder. 'What about your dad?'

June doubled over, heaving gut-wrenching sounds and strands of bile.

'Stop it, June!' May roused. 'An' you stop that silly crying, Ollie! Is he dead?'

'No!' June howled, backhanding spittle from her chin.

'Git the key!' May threatened Olive with a raised hand. 'Go on! Git!'

June sobbed. 'His leg … his leg is bust in half!'

Pushing June—'Git in! Damn ya!'—May climbed into the driver's seat, took the key from Olive. 'Git in! An' stop that stupid cryin'! Won't be no use to no one, bawling ya eyes out!'

The Plymouth jerked forward, lurched onto the road.

Leaning her head against Olive, June shut her eyes. 'There's blood!' She exhaled a shaky breath. 'An' busted bone sticking clean out of his leg.'

*

Fletcherview: New Year 1967

So that's how come Granddad Dick got a busted leg when *things started to go wrong*, and maybe it was because Granddad got a busted leg that the Widow Maker caught up with him sometime after that.

'You kids git! Take that melon, an' git out on the lawn.'

Mum and the aunties are washing up, and catching up, and the kitchen is still warm with the smell of roast pork and potatoes and lively with the clatter of the dishes and chatter.

I run through the kitchen to the laundry and I'm scooping a cup of Denkavit into the milk bucket when Aunty Melva calls out, 'What're ya doin'?'

'Gonna make some milk for Snowflake!'

'Better go an' check 'im first.'

Aunty Melva's right, so I run back through the kitchen through the dining room and I pull up short when I see Granny snoozing on the veranda in her squatter's chair. Granny's got her feet up on the leg rests; there's a *Women's Weekly* lying open on her big chest and Granny's little snores are fanning the corner of a page. I don't want to wake her up and make her cranky, so I tiptoe past Granny snoozing and run out to the Christmas tree.

Snowflake looks very still. Big green blowies are buzzing about the gashes on his legs, and houseflies are crawling in the black poop around his tail and bum.

I kneel down. Snowflake's eyes are milky-blue; meat-ants are crawling on his tongue and crawling between the little white baby teeth I was frightened of this morning. *Poor little baby.* I flap, and the flies buzz angrily and settle again. *Poor little fella.* I brush the meat-ants away and look up through the twisted branches of the Christmas tree and I have a word with God: I'm all for chuckin' sinners into hellfire, God; I'm all for wicked people moanin' and groanin' and beatin' their chests in hell, but what's that got to do with little Snowflake? The only sin Snowflake ever done was being caught by a pack of bloody mongrel dingoes—and that's gotta be *your* mistake, God, not Snowflake's. Seems to me Snowflake didn't have much of a life to flash before his eyes as he was dying, so can't ya bring him back? *Please!*

God's got nothing to say.

The limbs of the Christmas tree are magical: the bark comes off in summer and it's got a mottled look with patches of pink and grey and brown. It's a beautiful tree God made but Snowflake is still lying dead under it with ants and flies crawling on his tongue.

We can bury Snowflake here. Right here, beneath the Christmas tree. And cover the grave with purple blossom. I'll make a cross with pine fronds and—

I have the funeral fully planned when I see Jan coming. Jan's carrying an axe halfway down the wooden grip, and the axe head is swinging with her stride.

'Snowflake's dead,' I call to Jan. 'He's dead.'

'Told ya.'

'We can bury him right here—'

'Nah,' Jan says.

'What are ya gonna do with 'im?'

'Dad says we can feed 'im to the pigs.'

I watch the axe head swing up. Can't bear to watch it fall.

I run across the veranda yelling, 'Muuum!' I run inside yelling, 'Mummm!'

Dad's in the dining room playing chess with Uncle Ian and eating scorched almonds. Uncle Ian's pokey-out eyebrows are twitching and Dad's got his head in both hands, looking at the board down his crooked nose.

'Dad!'

Dad looks up. 'She's upstairs having a lie down, so don't you—'

'Mum!' All the kids are eating watermelon out there on the lawn. I run up the stairs with my head on sideways—I don't want them to see me crying—and throw myself on Mum and cry.

'What's up, love?' Mum says, pulling herself up on one elbow. 'What's happened?'

I bury my face against Mum's ribs. 'Snowflake's dead!'

Mum says, 'Don't cry, sweetheart, little Snowflake's happy now in heaven.'

I sit up and bawl, 'But she didn't have to chop 'im up!'

Mum settles back against the pillow, makes me comfortable in the crook of her arm, but after a while she says, 'Stop it now, Pammie, you're old enough to know that these things happen in the bush.'

I'm almost cried out, so I throw a leg across my mum and an arm around her waist and tell her, 'I don't wanna be a bushie anymore.'

We lie for a long time and you can hear the tin roof creak and pop in the heat. I'm thinking how my dad got his crooked nose when he was a boy. He was pretending to be a horse one day and ran around a corner slap-bang into a lamp-post and bust his nose … wish I was a horse.

I am almost asleep when I feel Mum move away.

I cling to her more tightly. 'Don't go!'

'I'm not going, sweetheart, but it's much too hot.'

I wriggle sideways a little bit; the sheets are damp with sweat.

Mum is looking up at the lacy valance, and I ask her what she's thinking.

'Just thinking that tonight my baby will be sleeping in the same bed I was born in.'

'In this bed?' I sit up on my elbow. 'But Granny didn't even *own* Fletcherview then.'

Mum says, 'Grandma caught the mail truck coming in from Niall; it was a hundred mile on rough dirt roads to get into town, so maybe that's why I came early. In any case, the mailman stopped here at Fletcherview and flagged down a passing car to take a message in to Dr Edmeads, but by the time he got here, I'd already been born.'

I lie back and look up at the lace valance of the mosquito net. It's an amazing feeling, lying with your mum in the same bed your mum was born in. I try to imagine nearly forty years ago, Granny Chapman lying here with a little baby girl crying in her arms. But I can't. In my head, Mum is still Mum and Granny is still cranky ol' Granny.

'And it was right here on Fletcherview you met Dad, wasn't it, Mum—when he was chopping wood? And later you got jealous because you thought he was only coming up to Fletcherview to visit Peggy?'

Mum holds the lace curtain back from the casement window, but there's not a breath of air anywhere.

'You were feeding the chooks, weren't you, Mum, when you saw a hobo coming down along that road? And you were scared at first because Grandma and the other girls were up at the cattle yards because Granddad Dick was still in hospital with his busted leg and the hobo didn't have a swag or anything but one arm in a sling, but it wasn't a hobo it was my dad needin' some pepper ...'

Mum goes, 'Mmmm.'

I turn to the window and look up along the red-dirt road; in the heat-shimmering stillness of the afternoon I can almost see my dad coming down along that red road with one arm in a sling.

And I think my mum might be seeing him too.

*

63

Fletcherview: February 1944

'Damn!' Fred lowered the rifle.

A cloud of yellow-crested cockatoos rose screeching skyward; shock waves echoing between the steep banks sent a heavily tusked boar barrelling into a clump of rubber vine. The mob, wallowing in the muddy shallows, set off helter-skelter.

A second shot, come from further along the bank, dropped a sow, and a dozen squalling piebald piglets crested the rise and scattered every which way into the scrub behind the camp.

Fred gave Bert the thumbs up, but Bert held his rifle up and called, 'See ya!'

Fred didn't see his brother slither down the bank; Fred was running back to camp. He'd heard it too: a jeep was coming. He ducked under the fly, kicked off his boots and hastily tucked three yellow tins out of sight under his swag.

Fred Bagnall, army reserve seconded to cut wood for the boilers down at the Charters Towers' weir, was sitting on the stump outside his tent sharpening an axe when the jeep found its way out of the scrub and parked beside his Chev.

Fred recognised the driver: Tom something-or-other—it wasn't the first time the MPs had come to call. Tom killed the engine, and a hard-faced MP in the passenger seat climbed out and strolled over to the bank. Shading his eyes, he searched along the deep watercourse in both directions. He wasn't in a hurry; he knew they'd never catch Bert Bagnall—not in this rugged country.

Tom went through the motions. He circled the remains of the camp fire, stuck his head under the fly and looked about inside the tent: a meat safe, a swag rolled out—one swag. 'You chopping by yerself?' he asked, dropping the canvas flap.

'Yeah.' Fred spat on his whetstone. 'Jack gave it away.'

'Can't say as I blame him.'

Fred concentrated on the axe, running the stone smoothly along the cutting edge. He wasn't worried about Bert: Bert was long gone—back to any one of his camps along Lolworth or further north along the banks of the Fletcher. Bert thought the whole catch-me-if-you-can he was playing with the army was a darned good joke.

For his part, Tom was openly appraising the fugitive's younger brother: khaki shorts, no shirt, no hat, nose broken in some bar-room brawl by the look of it. And brown! His skin was the colour of wet leather, and the muscled shoulders spoke of long hours wielding an axe beneath an unforgiving sun. All in all, Tom reckoned, Fred Bagnall was one tough-looking son of a bitch—and camped out here living like a blackfella. Still, the camp was tidy; there was a camp oven still half full of stew on the remains of the fire, and an old Chev 4—old, but in good order. Leaned against an ironbark were several well-maintained axes, a rifle, and a curious-looking stick: a small square piece of timber at one end was spiny with the points of nails. 'Catching fish?' he asked, touching it with his boot.

'Snakes,' Fred said shortly.

Squinting against the noon-day sun, Tom plucked a stalk of grass. 'They still shunting you between the railway and the army, Fred?'

Fred nodded, but the corner of his eye was tracking the size-twelve boots of the MP; those boots were scouting the perimeter of the clearing.

Checking they were out of earshot, Tom hunkered down, and confided: 'He was seen in town three times last week: Thursday night at the pictures and Friday at the sing-a-long in the ANA Hall; on Saturday he was seen in the crowd listenin' to the Salvos Band near the White Horse Hotel. Was winking at the tambourine girls, they say.'

Fred glanced up; the boy's eyes were sparkling with the mischief of it all. But the size-twelve boots had stopped at a patch of freshly turned earth ...

'Heard yer mum's running a guesthouse above Charlie Stapleton's store in Gill Street,' Tom remarked. 'Heard Bert likes to visit sometimes.'

Fred met the young man's eye, acknowledging the warning. 'Cuppa tea?' he returned. 'Was just about to put the billy on. Got stew left over too, kangaroo tail.'

The size-twelve boots were scuffing suspiciously at the loose dirt. 'What's this?'

'Old toilet hole an' scrap heap,' Fred answered. 'Just about to shift camp.'

The boots grunted and moved off quickly.

'Nice spot yer got here,' Tom said. 'Close to water an' all.'

'Beautiful spot,' Fred agreed. 'It's an anabranch,' he added, waving the whetstone in the general direction of the junction. 'Takes the overflow of Big Sandy down there and the backup water when the Burdekin's in flood. Spent a lot of time camped here trappin' possums in '36.'

The big boots were in no mood for small talk. 'Heard two shots.'

'Pigs,' Fred said. 'Big sow in that gulley over there. Fresh kill,' he added. 'No way I can eat 'er by meself ...

'Plenty more where she came from,' Fred was saying, as he helped manhandle the carcass into the jeep, and he only breathed easy when the sound of the engine faded into the scrub. *Damn!* He hadn't been worried about Bert; it was those three crates of American-issue Tropical Surprise—broken crates from a shipment being railed down from Darwin and left on the platform at the Charters Towers railway station. Theft was theft, even though the whole shipment was going to be jettisoned. He'd intended to shift camp this morning—after burying those crates of tinned butter— but the old Chev wouldn't start: radiator had sprung a leak. He'd been on the point of hoofing it the three mile up to Fletcherview to beg or borrow some pepper to plug it, when Bert turned up out of the blue ... and the pigs ... and so it went.

In the tent, Fred recovered the three tins of Tropical Surprise he'd kept out for his mum, sat down on his swag and was pulling on a boot when his heart froze: the blanket had moved. In an instant he was on his feet, axe in one hand, snake-catcher in the other.

Slowly, he put the snake-catcher aside, had the axe raised double-handed above his head when he heard the strangest noise: something between a squeak and a whimper.

Cautiously, he leaned down, flicked the blanket back, and breathed relief. The piebald piglet squealed pathetically, and tried to nose its way under the swag. He caught hold of the tiny lump beneath the blanket; she bucked and squealed as he held her up in one hand. It wasn't likely she'd survive: all skin and bone, and so small she had to be the runt. And his priority right now was getting up to Fletcherview—without pepper for the radiator, Fred Bagnall wouldn't be going into town tonight; without pepper, Fred Bagnall wouldn't be watching Fred Astaire and Ginger Rogers in *Top Hat* screening at the Olympia.

Fred studied the piglet face to face. He had plenty of condensed milk, and he supposed he could fashion a sling to carry her ...

'Come on then, Peggy,' he said. 'Let's you and me go and get some pepper.'

5

A piece of bone

Fletcherview: 1968

Bartlams Ltd is a single-storey brick and stucco building built at the turn of the century when Charters Towers was booming, pop: 27,000, but after the Great War, houses in Charters Towers disappeared at the rate of one every two days, and the railway was kept busy.

Nowadays, Bartlams is a bulk grocery and hardware store for rural families, and the shed on the other side of the gravelled yard out back is for stock and vet supplies.

Bartlams is Granny's last stop on the way out of town. Granny puts her order in when she drives into town on Friday mornings, and we're here picking up Granny's order on our way out of town this afternoon.

'Come on, you kids,' Granny says, throwing up the canvas. 'Git outta there.'

Richard and David grab the backboard and jump down in one go. Betty and Judith, Jackie, Alison and Jan climb over and jump down; I climb over the backboard too, but I feel about with my foot till I find the bumper bar and jump down from there.

At Bartlams they've all been waiting for Granny; you can set your watch at three thirty, when Granny's old grey Land Rover pulls in and parks against the loading platform in the side alley. The big wooden landing is ready with grocery boxes and drums, and when Mrs Chapman pulls into the alley, a whole lot of men and young working boys in white shirts and navy-blue bibbed aprons down to their knees come running with two-wheel lifter trolleys.

Us kids all stand out of the way, leaning back against the big landing, as they load up the Rover with Granny's weekly order. There are only eight kids going to Granny's for the holidays this year because there've been some changes: mainly, my big sister Robyn can't come to Granny's because Robyn's finished Grade Ten at St Gabes—got straight As on her Junior Certificate—and got a job doing the books for P&E, the local supermarket.

Jan and me started Grade Four at St Gabes but then we had to go to All Souls. And of all the changes the worst, by far the *worst*, is Brother Robin.

'Afternoon, Mrs Chapman.'

You never hear anyone call Granny by her first name; even men old as Granny never call her 'May'. It's always, 'Yes, Mrs Chapman; No, Mrs Chapman; Three bags full, Mrs Chapman.' The three bags are cracked corn, wheat and a laying mash. There are no seats in the back of Granny's Land Rover so there's plenty of room, and the Rover rocks as the men heft the big bags in. Because *big stuff's gotta go in first*. A bag of sugar and one of flour are thrown in, and the Rover rocks some more as the men drag them crosswise onto the bags of chook feed. Four big boxes of groceries, then a bundle of star-picket iron posts clangs on the metal floor and is shoved in alongside a drum of cattle dip. Lighting fuel is loaded last: there's kerosene for the fridge and the lamps upstairs, a drum of carbide for the lights used in the kitchen and the dining room, and metho for cleaning.

'I think that's it, Mrs Chapman.' A man slams the backboard shut, takes off his hat.

'Come on, you kids.' Granny glances at the silver watch pinned on her dress. 'Don't wanna to be late gettin' the men their smoko.'

Big Granny pulls herself up and behind the steering wheel; us kids climb in the back, find a good spot on one of the bags. We're headed out of town when David tells Richie, 'He's gonna get rocked if he gets caught. He's gonna get rocked, big time!' Ever since David started school at All Souls, where everyone has a nickname, kids all call him *Dough-arse*. I don't. *Dough-arse* is a rude name.

'Brother Mattingly rocked him six, 'cause that's the most he's allowed to give.'

I go to All Souls now. I've seen little kids get rocked.

You only really know it's holidays when we pass the cemetery and the bitumen becomes dirt road. That's when we start singing, and David gets first choice: he knows all the words of 'Beverly Hillbillies'. We *still* don't have a TV! But sometimes on Sunday arvo, Dad still takes me over to the Paines', and my best favourite of all is still *Mr Ed*, the talking horse.

When it's my turn to pick a song, I pick 'Miss Polly had a dolly' because on the last day of school, down at my old school, we put a concert on, and I did Miss Polly and Noel Griffiths did the doctor. But the other kids all say 'Miss Polly' is a little kid's song and they're not gonna sing it, so I sing it: *Miss Polly had a dolly who was sick, sick, sick, so she called for the doctor to be quick, quick, quick.*

And the other kids all yell, 'Shuddup! shuddup! shuddup!'

Wish I was still going to Millchester State.

St Gabriels is a Church of England girls school. Mum went to St Gabes when she was a girl but in Mum's day nuns ran it, and Mum really liked the nuns, especially Sister Bernardino and

Sister Hope, but the nuns all went broke so now normal people run it. During the Depression, my dad flattened some of the sports fields at the schools doing relief work with a shovel. During the war my dad didn't get a medal for, the Japs came over and dropped some bombs on Townsville, so the Yanks came over too and took over all the schools in Charters Towers for hospitals. The girls at St Gabes had to go to school at a Royal Hotel in Richmond and the boys from All Souls all went and camped in their pyjamas on Gainsford on the Burdekin, where my mum used to live when she was really little. At Gainsford, the boys lived in tents and caught black bream in the river and weren't allowed to go home, not even for Christmas, but after two years they went and lived in the horse stables on the racecourse and watched the Yank planes coming back from the Coral Sea with parts missing.

I guess going to St Gabes *started* well enough; but it all really *started* one day when the Grade Fours and Fivers were called up to the office to see the headmistress. 'You girls are very lucky,' Mrs Beard told us. 'You're going to get on the bus every day and go over to All Souls for your lessons. Won't that be lovely?'

Even little kids heard Gabes was going broke—just like the nuns went broke in Mum's day—but whatever the case, fifteen little girls sitting in a little green bus with wooden platform seats in our yellow uniforms and our brown school bags with a gold crest on the side aren't very happy about the whole shemozzle of going to an all-boy school. And we find out soon enough no one is as unhappy as Brother Robin is unhappy about the whole shemozzle.

We get off the bus and the Grade Fivers go round to another building and Matron leads us Grade Fours with our bags under the stairs of a double-storey Queenslander. The classroom is full of boys all craning their necks and gawking at us, and Matron lines us up in pairs, even though there are only five of us in Grade Four. I'm holding Jan's hand and even Jan's hand is trembling too.

71

There's a scary tall man in the classroom. His black robe comes almost to the floor and is tied at the waist with a red rope, and the scary man is spinning the knots on the end of his red rope in a circle. I see a broad-brimmed black hat on the teacher's desk at the front of the classroom, and his scythe must be in one of the big cupboards over there because he's only got a blackboard ruler. He taps the ruler on the concrete between his boots. 'Oh,' he says, acting like he's surprised to see us or maybe like we're very late. 'So, you've arrived, have you?' He's got a red face, and looks like a hawk: got a big hook nose and some hair on the back half of his head and he's looking at us down his big beak nose. 'Run along then,' he tells Matron.

I've never seen Matron run before—you only ever see Matron waddle—but this day Matron runs along and leaves us all on our own with the Widow Maker's second cousin.

'Come along then!' he says, waving at two empty desks up the back.

Us girls scuttle in with our bags, but there are only four chairs at the two desks! Jan and Lucy and Sharon and me get there first, and Shelly tries to push her little bottom in on my chair with me, which is really silly because Shelly can't sit on my chair with me and I push her off.

Shelly's got to find her own chair at a desk with three boys, and I'm really sorry I pushed Shelly off my chair but it's each man for himself.

The classroom is silent. The boys are staring at us. Us girls are staring at our desks, but I make the mistake of looking up at him. He's looking down at me with one eye like a pirate; he's got a bushy eyebrow high up on his slanty forehead and the other bushy eyebrow is covering his other eye. 'I don't like females!' he says, shortening his red twirling rope so it twirls faster.

I look down and I'm looking at the shiny toe-caps of his boots because he's come to stand at our desk and my heart feels like it knows it's gonna get sucked out. 'In particular,' he says, rocking on his toes, 'I don't like females with bags!' He kicks my schoolbag with his boot and I pull it out of the way under my desk.

'And in particular, particular,' he says, 'I don't like females who push their shopping bags against my back. They used to, you know? Ah, yes,' he says, rocking on his toes and twirling his red rope, 'in the shopping queues, standing on the bus: big females pushing their shopping bags against a little boy's back!'

I think maybe he's just funnin'? I glance up. Maybe not.

He makes a snorting sound through his nose, then says, 'Wonder how many choruses I'll have to sing today?'

It's some sort of cue, because the boys all get busy opening books and getting pencils.

'Natural,' he says, twirling his red rope. 'It's not *natural* to have little girls at a boys school.' The boys all start writing, but us girls have to scrabble in our bags under our desks to get our books and pencils out.

'School,' he says. 'It's not natural, for girls to be at an all-boys *school.*'

He says twenty words, and not hard words, so Jan and me catch up. Then the boys all swap books, so us girls all swap books, and correct our words round the class. When all the boys stand up in their places without being asked, us girls stand up too.

'Twenties,' he says, and some boys sit down, so Jan and me look at each other and sit down because we got twenty, but Sharon and Lucy and little Shelly are still standing.

He gets the blackboard ruler in both hands and swings it, like testing the weight of a cricket bat. He does a slide step into a polka and starts singing, 'Row, row, row, your boats,' *WHACK!* He lands the big ruler on a boy's bum and the boy rocks forward on his toes.

And then the Widow Maker's second cousin is dancing round the classroom singing, 'Gently down the stream'—*WHACK!*

Shelly's little bum rocks forward and Shelly starts crying. 'Merrily, merrily, merrily'—*WHACK!* Sharon and Lucy start crying even before he whacked 'em. 'Life is but a dream ...'

We just passed Big Sandy so it's not far now to Granny's, and the other kids are singing, 'She'll be riding six white horses when she comes—when she comes!'

The Land Rover pulls into the drive, and Rover and Boxer are barking and pawing at the fence, and Boxer is a big dog now, but there's no sign of Sal. 'Where's ol' Sal, Grandma?' And Granny says how a big brown got ol' Sal, but not before ol' Sal got the big brown. Granny sounds real proud that ol' Sal with only one good eye got the big brown, but seems to me poor ol' Sal still got got!

Granny says, 'Just leave everything for the moment, you kids, I gotta help Melva git the men their smoko first, then yers can help me unload.'

Granny might be the centre of the universe, but life at Fletcherview revolves around the men. 'Gotta git up at four tomorra, the men'll be wantin' lunches cut; must put on a piece of corned meat tonight, the men'll be wantin' meat fer lunches; you girls hurry up an' git inta the bath, the men'll be here wantin' theirs d'rectly; which one of you boys want the bone to chew on?' (Granny still doesn't know us girls'd like—*just once!*—to get the roast bone to chew on.)

Aunty Melva's finishing up in the kitchen. It's pretty late but us kids are still up, because Granny's down at Lolworth Creek in the dark. Granny doesn't have electricity, so we've got the three carbide lights all up this end of Granny's big redwood table. There's carbide in the bottom of those tins, and in the top is a little reservoir of water; the water drips down on the carbide, making gas that makes those little flames so bright.

David just told a story about a lunatic who chopped a man's head off and left it on the hood of the car the girlfriend was sitting in on a lonely track, waiting on her boyfriend to come back with the petrol. Men always tell the best stories. Mostly women talk about babies and curtains; men talk about things that happen in the bush—like the mystery of what happened to Bollinger's gold, or min-min lights leading strangers off the beaten track, or black trackers who can track an ant across the Nullarbor. Uncle Owen's telling about an old blackfella who was just gonna kill a big boar pig with an axe, but the axe head flew off so the old blackfella only hit the pig with the handle and the pig ripped up the blackfella with his tusks.

Granny's got tame pigs in her pigpen and a big purebred pink boar called Big Joe, but Granny's got a pig trap for wild pigs down on the banks of Lolworth Creek. Granny lies down there all by her own in the dark—'No point in doin' it in moonlight.' Granny hates wild pigs. Pigs root up the ground but mainly because wild pigs have footrot fungus and carry things like brucellosis, tuberculosis, parvo, lepto—a whole load of things, but the only one I ever heard of is rabies because I cried when Travis had to shoot ol' Yeller when he got the rabies. I'd like to tell the story of ol' Yeller, but I don't get a turn, and foot and mouth disease is Granny's greatest worry for her cattle, not rabies.

Granny goes up to the cattle yards and down the bank to Lolworth before it gets really dark but she's still gotta come all the way back with a torch. If I was Granny, I'd make some of the big kids come down to the creek with me. Even sitting on the veranda can sometimes be scary at Fletcherview at night; there are always things creeping, crawling and scuttling in the bush, and sometimes you hear a dingo howl. When Granny hears a pig snuffling at the carcass the men put in the trap, all Granny's got to do is pull the rope and the fork stick drops and the door drops shut. One time, Granny caught seven wild pigs one night in the trap and the men shot them in the morning—Granny's got Uncle Owen as head stock-man, and only two ringers because it's hard finding good ringers these days—but Granny's been down a dozen times since and hasn't caught a single pig and I get to thinking, *What if a big boar pig with big tusks snuck up on Granny? Or a big brown snake, or a min-min light, flickering through the trees, or maybe there's a mental patient, escaped from Mosman Hall in town, and he's hiding out in the bush and he hasn't caught any wild pigs and he hasn't eaten for a week, an* ...

'What're you kids still doin' outta bed?'

Thank God Granny's still alive! Granny leans against the door-frame, puts the toe of one boot against the heel of the other boot to wriggle it off, then puts her toes against the first boot and wriggles it off. Granny's feet are all buggered up with bunions and corns; Granny's hammertoes ride on top of her big toes all knobbly. Mum says Granny's feet are all buggered up because Granny wore her shoes too tight when she was young, only Mum doesn't say 'buggered'. Mum never swears. Dad never swears either, except maybe with men.

'C'mon, you kids!' Granny says, all cranky. 'Git upstairs t' bed! Got a big day t'morra.'

'Didya get any, Granny?' asks Uncle Owen.

Uncle Owen's cheeky calling Granny 'Granny'—most everybody calls her Mrs Chapman. I asked Dad once, 'What do you call Granny?' Dad said he just waits till Granny's lookin'. I only ever heard Joe Downey call her 'May', but Granny won't marry Joe Downey even if he asks her.

*

Charters Towers Hospital: 17 March 1944

If ever you were in need of a good ringer, trapper, fencer, folks'd allas tell ya: *Just ask Joe Downey: If Joe Downey sends out a man, yer can be sure he's a good'un.*

Joe came from the Mingela–Ravenswood area, and had been in stock all his life. Joe was a gun horseman, good with racehorses, trotters, show horses—but Joe's eye for cattle was second to none. Joe knew what breeds grew best in what sort of country, and Joe was making a name for himself as a cattle buyer for Swift Australia Pty Ltd. In 1941, Joe bought 4910 bullocks and 2520 fat cows from eighty-two different properties in the Charters Towers district—and travelled as far south as Rockhampton, and to Mareeba in the north. Most times Joe drove out to the property, borrowed a horse and rode the cattle, estimating dressed weight of anything up to a thousand head at a time. In 1956, an official statement from Swifts—the owners of the meatworks at Alligator Creek outside Townsville—will state that Joe Downey inspected and bought 6804 bullocks and was down 3.78 pounds in his total estimates, and down 1.62 pounds on 2087 fat cows. Joe will say he must be slipping in 1961: in '61 the works will kill 68,000 head and Joe will be eleven pounds out in his overall estimation.

'Thanks, Joe.' Olive slanted him a look and handed him the mirror.

Joe had just taken over mirror-holding duties for Dick, only to find there wasn't much thanks in it. Dick Chapman was not a happy man. Two and a half months, Dick Chapman had been lying in this bed; the only view his leg strung up, heel pinned on a weird contraption of pulleys and weights. The leg was lying straight now in a full-length plaster cast. But Dick Chapman wouldn't be coming home for *at least another month*. And even then, he'd *have a short plaster on his leg.*

Dulcie and Olive had been taking turns—week in, week out— to stay in town at Spargo's Boarding House, so Dick always had someone come to visit. Between the hours of nine and ten in the morning and seven and eight at night, Dick had plenty of visitors. Dick had plenty of home-grown grapes and oranges piled up on the night stand, but Dick Chapman was not a happy man. Thank God Joe dropped by when he could.

Olive liked Joe Downey. He was a strapping man, wore gabardine stockman-cut riding pants, a crisp white shirt and high-heeled R.M. Williams riding boots—and already walked just a little bit bandy like older bush men did. Joe keeping her dad up to date with cattle talk this evening had let Olive off the hook. Her mind was in such a dither, she couldn't seem to concentrate on anything. She glanced up at the wall clock: ten to eight; the bell would ring shortly and the matron would come and chase the visitors, and Olive would walk the two blocks back to the boarding house. And he'd said he *might* be in town tonight.

Olive was pulling on her new gloves when Dick put down the shaving blade and wiped his face. 'What are you up to, missy?'

'Nothing.' Olive glanced at the clock. 'Just … nothing.'

'Keep an eye on this one, Dick,' Joe kidded, putting down the mirror and clearing the shaving gear. 'Pretty as a picture, and dressed to kill.'

'I am not!' Olive said self-consciously, but she hoped she was pretty. Her cotton dress, printed with yellow-hearted frangipanis, was pretty—cost three ducks and a dozen eggs.

Dick was eyeing her closely. 'You'll go straight round to Spargo's, won't you, Ollie?'

'Course I will!'

The visiting bell sounded. Olive's heart skipped and she wished June were here: she couldn't very well ask her dad or Joe Downey to check her stocking seams were straight.

'Promise?' Dick squeezed her gloved hand.

'You know I will.' Olive kissed her dad goodnight. 'No, thank you, Joe, I don't need anyone to walk me; it's just around the corner.'

*

T'enni rate, Emily Bagnall could smell a rat.

'You're a good boy, Fred,' Emily was saying as he got down from the chair.

Emily walked around her little kitchen checking the top shelf from all directions—checking that the three yellow tins of Tropical Surprise were *outta sight ahind them empty orange Weet-Bix tins, Fred,* that Emily was keeping on the top shelf up there *'cause them orange Weet-Bix tins'll be hair-looms one day, Fred.*

He was a good boy, her Fred, always looking out for his mum, so Emily didn't have the heart to tell him, 'War or no war, Emily Bagnall wouldn't feed that Yankee substitute butter to a goat.' Not that Emily had a goat anymore; Emily was well set up in her little guesthouse in Charters Towers. What with old George gone to Cardwell to find work, Emily's little guesthouse, above Charlie Stapleton's store in Gill Street, had turned out to be *just the ticket* for Emily and her youngest, little Dorrie, who played tambourine for the Salvos.

Emily went to the window, tweaked the curtain and looked down to check the main street before turning back to her boys. Fred was leaning against the doorjamb watching Bert, who was wolfing down a plate of Emily's corned beef *with lots of fat on just like yer like it, Bertie,* boiled jacket potatoes *an' lotsa proper butter an' some fresh cabbage I got from ol' Ah Pan an' cost a pretty penny.*

Emily liked nothing better than her boys come to visit, but she was wishing it wasn't tonight: Emily had been looking forward to catching Clark Gable in *Mutiny on the Bounty*. 'If yer goin' to the pictures, Fred, yer gonna miss the start.' Emily tweaked the curtain again, and glanced down at the street. 'Well what are ya doing in town then? Not like you to miss *The Mutiny.*'

Emily could definitely smell a rat: well past seven and Fred still hanging about like a bad penny—not like Fred at all. No doubt Fred had scrubbed up well, *and* he kept glancing at the clock.

Emily just hoped it wasn't some floosie had caught Fred's eye. Seemed to Emily there were lots of floosies these days—women dropping their knickers all over the place for soldiers. But Fred wouldn't have no time for floosies; Fred didn't have no time for the sort of women can create mess in their own lives and in the lives of respectable others.

T'enni rate, Emily had long since given up on *gettin' any grand-kids outta Fred.* Shy, Fred was. *Ah, well. Leastways he's got a little pig for company livin' out there in the bush.*

Emily tweaked the curtain and—

'Bert!' she said urgently, waving Bert away with one hand.

Bert jumped up, took one stride, and his back was against the wall near the kitchen door; Fred hooked the door shut with a foot, slid into Bert's place at the table. All three listened to the sound of boots running up both front and back stairs.

Fred had a forkful of Bert's corned beef midway to his mouth when the door burst open—hiding Bert behind it.

'Cuppa tea, boys?' Emily asked the MPs. 'Just about to put the kettle on.'

*

On the hospital steps, Olive opened her purse and fumbled for her lipstick; wondered if *he* might think it macabre—keeping a piece of her dad's bone in the little bottle in her purse.

In the silence of the night, she could hear someone whistling a familiar tune: 'Leaning on a lamp-post'. Down there at the hospital gate, standing under the streetlight, was a man …

It was him! And he was waiting just for her.

Heart beating wildly, she closed her eyes and tried to hold the moment—this moment in time which marked the beginning of the rest of her life …

She asked how Peggy was doing, and Fred told her, 'Fine.'

He asked how her dad was doing, and Olive told him, 'Fine.'

Fred wondered if she might like to go and listen to the Salvos, playing down at the White Horse Hotel. Olive wondered how childish she must have sounded: *I told my dad I'd go straight round to Spargo's ...*

'I'm staying at Spargo's Boarding House, near the Bowls Club.'

'I know.'

'How do you know?'

'I asked.'

Olive hid her smile. *Was there ever a girl in all the world?*

They crossed Church Street and Fred was wondering how much longer the war would go on. Olive was wondering when he would try to hold her hand. And should she let him? They were walking close enough—close enough for his sleeve to brush her shoulder, close enough for her to smell the fresh smell of him and soap.

Ahead, a few late window shoppers were strolling arm in arm, like lovers.

Could he feel it too? How every step drew them closer?

She supposed she *might* put her hand in the crook of his elbow?

Overwhelming thought.

He touched her elbow, briefly, as they passed through a group of people gathered on the footpath listening to war news on a loudspeaker.

Fred was wondering how long petrol rationing would continue. Olive was wondering how it was possible to feel as though you'd known someone all your life, but know nothing about him. Nothing but that he'd carried a baby pig in a sling and called it Peggy.

And thinking that he was taller than she remembered.

At Fletcherview it had been easier. Olive had told him, 'Come on in, I've got a baby bottle.' But, finding she was home alone, Fred had waited at the gate. Handing him the bottle, she'd dared look into his eyes: blue-grey, shy eyes that had slid back to the safety of a little pig. That was the moment she'd felt a tremor, a vibration, infinitesimal but absolute; that was the moment she'd *known*. But it had been easier with Peggy between them: they'd both kept their eyes on the little pig, and not on each other; they'd both stroked and petted the little pig, and not ...

Shocking thought!

Fred wondered what would be playing next week at the Olympia. Olive was wondering how it was that in any romantic fantasy she'd always seen herself as Janet Gaynor; why then, tonight, did she feel like Greta Garbo? How was it she could feel so tight and light and bubbly and happy and so ... desirable?

Outrageous thought!

They turned at the corner, shoulders touching. The street, and a warm and balmy night lay ahead. A balmy night where darkness amplified touch, hearing, smell: the brush of his arm against her arm; the faint strains of the band playing down at the White Horse Hotel; the smell of fresh-mown bowling green, night-flowering jasmine, soap ... overall and everywhere, him.

It was as though she understood everything she'd ever read, thought or heard about men and women; in this altered state, she felt so small that she was infinite: a girl bearing witness to the mystery of her life unfolding, a life so small, so inconsequential, so significant.

Was he feeling it too, this yearning to lean in against him?

Spargo's lay ahead. And Fred had fallen silent.

They were walking so slowly now that they may not have been walking at all.

Spargo's gate. It was confusing how those light, bubbly feelings could so quickly dissipate. Why hadn't he held her hand? He hadn't even tried! And she'd worn her new dress tonight—cost three ducks and a dozen eggs—and he hadn't even noticed! And why had he talked about the war and rationing and chopping wood and movies? And why was it that he'd fallen to humming to himself? And how was it she could feel so happy one moment and the prick of tears the next?

He opened the gate; his face, backlit, was in shadow.

Did she turn to him? Or did he pull her in?

He kissed her—hard. She slapped him—hard.

He said, 'I'm sorry!' She said, 'I'm sorry!'

Fred knew what common sense would do, but common sense only speaks to those with ears to listen.

Taking both her hands, he asked, 'Can I walk you home tomorrow night?'

He watched her run up the steps, waited until she had closed the door before he rubbed his cheek. For such a small girl, Olive May Chapman delivered quite a wallop.

Imagining the next night, Frederick Francis Bagnall was whistling as he strolled away; then, humming along with George Formby— could even hear the banjolele, and he couldn't resist the words: 'Leaning on a lamp-post ...'

*

Charters Towers: 1968

We go back to school, and I got two things. First thing I got is Big Joe's fault, and the second thing I got is a mysterious illness. The first thing is I got nits—just the same as I got nits when we went back to school last term. I tell Mum I hate St Gabes, and what can you expect making me go to a boarding school where all the little girls have nits!

Only, Matron looks in all the little girls' heads, and seems like I'm the only little girl got the nits. I make Matron pull all

83

the sheets off all the beds, but we don't find no nits—only I tell Matron I might've seen one because I don't wanna be the little girl spreading nits.

We've got no idea where the nits came from, but next Friday when Granny Chapman comes to town, Granny says, 'What can ya expect when yer go lying round in the pigpen!' I love lying in Granny's pigpen. Big Joe is Granny's big pink boar and when Big Joe sees me coming he lies down and I lie on Big Joe and scratch his belly and he grunts. Granny says I got pig lice climbed into my hair from scratching on Big Joe's belly so that's why I have to go to school with DDT-oily hair for a week.

The second thing is the mysterious illness—comes on every morning when we're having breakfast at the cafe. At around eight o'clock I start feeling sick. Some days I throw up into Lenny the pigman's scrap bins and Mum says I don't have to go to school and takes me to the doctor.

Mum says we've got to get to the doctor before lunchtime and I say, 'Why have we got to get to the doctor before lunchtime when I'll probably be feeling better by lunchtime?' And Mum says Doc's a good doctor but Doc's only good till about lunchtime.

The doctor is not good ol' Doc Ellis put nine stitches in my head and fished out the tooth Robyn kicked down my throat. Doc Ellis is retired.

I heard people call the new doctor Mick Bogtrotter but most people call him Doc.

Doc came out all the way from Ireland in a big cowboy hat, cowboy boots and a leather vest, just like Little Joe in *Bonanza*. Seems Doc was going to America but he came to Australia because he heard no one in Australia minds if you ride a horse to work and no one in Australia minds if you get legless. A big hospital in Brisbane minded Doc riding his horse to work and getting legless, so Doc came to Charters Towers, where no one minds anything.

Doc bought himself a creamy pony and married himself a little Charters Towers widow to look after him. She looked after him real well for a time—but when Doc got kicked out of his private practice and went to work at the hospital, he's only got to cross the street to the Sovereign Hotel, and about lunchtime everyday Doc crosses the street. The man who owns the pub lets Doc keep his pony in the backyard. At ten o'clock at night the man picks Doc up and puts him on his creamy pony and the pony knows his way back to his paddock in the dark. And it's a good thing Doc is legless because sometimes when he gets home Doc gives it to his wife, but only if she's been asking for it and only if he can catch her.

Doc says I've got a bug in my tummy and gives me white medicine. When that doesn't work, next time he stands me between his knees, and he takes my hands and asks real gentle, 'Is something upsetting you?' He's so kind I feel like crying, but I don't. How can I tell him Brother Robin doesn't like little girls? And, *in particular, particular* little girls who do better in exams than little boys ...

The third time Mum takes me to see Doc before lunch, he gives me little blue pills and tells Mum I've got a nervous disposition. I suppose I must have a disposition because I really, *really* wanted to get Brother John in Grade Five but Brother John's not at All Souls anymore—talk among the big girls is Brother John ran off with the drama teacher.

But after a time Brother Robin gets used to having little girls in his classroom and we get used to Brother Robin singing *Row, row, row, your boat* first thing every morning. It's not so hard because he gives us the words to learn for prep, and the other little girls don't cry so much when they get whacked and sometimes not at all. But he's still always acting like he's in a drama play: waving with his arms and sometimes pretending to cry when a kid does something stupid. But most times you can work out when he's making fun and when he isn't.

So anyway, one day Jan and me are sitting on the steps with a boy called Delilah waiting for the milkman to come with our little bottles of milk we get every day at little lunch—they call it recess at All Souls—and Stuart comes and stands in front of us. Stuart's a Grade Six boy does wicked things to cats and Stuart's got his arms folded and his feet planted wide like he's a man, and Stuart says to me, 'John wants to go with you.' I grab Jan's hand and we run away.

But the next day at little lunch Stuart comes and stands in front of us, folds his arms across his chest, plants his feet and says, 'John wants to go with you.' Same thing on the third day, but this day Stuart says, 'Do ya wanna go with 'im or not?' John doesn't look too ugly from a distance, so I say I'll only go with John if he buys me the china palomino pony in Pershouse the Jeweller's shop window I go and look at every day. After the weekend, Stuart comes and gives me the china pony and I'm in love with the palomino pony but not so much with John.

John comes and sits beside me at little lunch. He's got a cold. Not a sniff-sniff kind of cold, more a snotty-gobble, suck-back, swallow kind of cold. I grab Jan's hand and run away. John tells Stuart to tell me he wants his pony back. I tell Mum, 'A boy gave me this palomino pony and now he wants his pony back because I won't sit with him.'

Mum says, 'Well, do you like him, honey?'

I say, 'Not really.'

And Mum says, 'You really can't take little china ponies from boys you don't like.'

So next day at school I give the pony back and the next day after that Stuart comes and tells me John smashed the little china pony I loved so much with a hammer.

That other boy's name, the one we were sitting with that first day, isn't really Delilah. His name is Sam Kelly, but Sam made

86

the mistake of telling the other boys his name was Samson and he doesn't like being called Sam—so now they call him Delilah when they're teasing and Del when they aren't.

Poor Samson Kelly has nothing going for him anyway: it isn't his fault, but Sam is the only South African in a school full of boys from outback Queensland. Sam can't ride a horse, let alone a bullock; Sam can't brand a calf, drive a four-wheel drive or shoot a pig; Sam has no interest in football or cricket. Sam's a big, tubby boy a head taller than the boys in our class and tries to hide the fact by getting around with his shoulders slumped like he's looking for answers on his big tummy stuck out in front of him.

To tell the truth, he has a nice face but it is round and soft and the skin on his nose is always red and peeling. And everyone *knows* Grade Four boys wear elastic-waisted shorts, and everyone *knows* you wear your shorts on your hips. Sam has to wear the belted kind of shorts the senior boys wear, and he wears them belted above his big tummy. He looks a bit like Humphrey B. Bear, but he isn't a bad kid, and he's happy enough to be left alone at little lunch. At recess you can see him sitting on the steps drawing in the back of his maths book. While Sam is sitting on the steps, other boys running down the stairs smack him on the head; if they're going up the stairs, they make a limp wrist and swing their hips like they think girls walk and say, 'Ooooh, Delilaaaah!'

One time, Sam showed me a dragon flying above a castle with flames coming out its nostrils. It was very good and I told Sam I thought his flying dragon was very good. I was nice to Sam—but only that one time.

This morning we're all lined up at the door and you just know something's wrong. The boys are all grinning and whispering: 'He's gonna get rocked! He's gonna get rocked big time!' From an interior door, *he* swoops into the classroom. He takes his time looking about at the crumpled paper and broken chalk scattered on the floor.

It's everywhere. The classroom's a mess and there's even scribble on *his* blackboard. He comes over to the door, makes a show of running a finger down the prep duty roster and then stopping on yesterday's date and SAMSON KELLY. He turns and puts both hands above him on the lintel so he's leaning out over Jan and me lined up. 'KELLY!' he roars, and there's just no way in hell he's funnin': his face is red and there's steam coming out his nostrils and little puffs coming out his ears.

Sam shoulders his way slowly up the centre of us kids lined up in pairs and by the time he reaches Jan and me, Sam's already whimpering.

'This!' He grabs Sam by the shoulders and turns him to face us. 'This!' He grabs a handful of hair and jerks Sam's face up for everyone to see. 'This is a lazy, LAZY boy!' He yanks Sam by the hair and Sam lets out a yowl, steps back, clips the step and almost falls but he's being held up by his hair. Sam's not even pretending to hold it in now: he's proper bawling. Sam tries to step up onto the step but *he* pushes Sam back down again. 'What are you? Go on! I want you to tell them all. What are you?'

'A lazy boy,' Sam whimpers.

He snigs Sam by the ear into the room, twists that ear till Sam kneels. 'Pick ... it ... up!'

Sam is crawling on his hands and knees around the bits of paper, but when he's got the bin half full, *his* boot kicks the bin and it slams against the wall and ricochets. Sam's got his hands up to protect his face but the bin catches his chin and there's some blood on his lip. He grabs Sam by the collar and the other hand grabs Sam's big pants and he throws Sam and there's a loud crash as desks and chairs tumble over and Sam's head smacks into the wall. We all move away from the door, but some of the boys are still craning their necks at the windows, trying to see. I don't want to see but I can hear.

'What are you?'

'A lazy boy.'

'What are you?'

Sam screams: 'A LAZY BOY!'

'A big, fat lump of a lazy boy! What are you? Say it!'

'A big, fat lump of a lazy boy.'

Even the boys aren't watching now. They got their hands stuffed in their pockets as they saunter away and stand in groups drawing patterns in the gravel with their shoe-caps and muttering.

I follow Jan over to the tennis court and watch the parrots up there, swinging upside-down in the palm tree. *It was just a mean joke, to get Sam rocked, can't he see that?* I like watching the parrots after school while we wait for the bus. *If I can see that, why can't he see that?* Sometimes in the afternoon they're drunk from eating rotting fruit, and they can be funny when they're drunk. *Why isn't he rocking all these other boys for being mean?* But sometimes a drunk parrot flies into the tennis fence. *And why aren't we all doing something?* And if he's badly stunned, you have to put him on the umpire's seat—*What are you?*—because he's got shade there, but mostly you put him up there so ants won't get to him before he wakes up with a headache. *A big, fat lump of a lazy boy!* They're rainbow lorikeets, those parrots. *What are you?* I know because one time, Dad took Mum down to Currumbin and there's this great photo of my mum with these birds sitting on her head and climbing on her arms and pecking at the seed dish she's holding. *A big fat lazy lump.* Mum is really beautiful smiling like that, and they're really beautiful, those birds. *What are you?* They've got a bright red beak, a blue head and belly, green wings and tail, and an orangey-yellow breast.

Say it!

Finally, Sam can't even say it. Finally, it is each man for himself.

Sam left All Souls at the end of the year. No one saw him, or heard from him again.

But I think of him sometimes, how I should've stood up for him.

Why? Because doing nothing feels ugly, no matter what your age.

6

Monday's child is full of woe

Christmas 1968

I hate Mondays.

Monday is wash day at Granny's; look closely, you'll see it inscribed on the stone tablet handed down to Moses on Mount Sinai: THOU SHALT WASH THY CLOTHES ON MONDAY!

'Don't go anywhere, you girls, yer can help with the washin',' Granny Chapman says as we're clearing breakfast. 'Yer can catch up with the men after smoko.'

David and Richard swagger out, riding boots clomp-clomp-clomping on cement.

And God looked down and spake unto them: GIRLS DO WASHING; BOYS DON'T! IT'S THE LAW! GIRLS DO WASHING-UP, MAKE BEDS, EMPTY PEE POTS: BOYS DON'T! IT'S THE LAW!

First day of the holidays, Betty does up a roster. Betty and Judith and Alison and Jackie do breakfast, lunch and dinner, but they're going to rotate it to make it fair because night-time roasts and desserts make the biggest wash-up.

I'm proud Betty showed me her roster. 'It's a good roster,' I tell Betty. 'I think it's very fair.'

And then Betty goes and says, 'An' you an' Jan do smokos.'

'But smoko's twice a day!' I say. 'Smoko comes morning and afternoon!'

'Smoko's just cups and saucers,' Betty says.

'And bread-and-butter plates! And most times Granny does cooking—that means baking trays and things! How come David and Richard don't have to do washin'-up?'

'Men don't do washin'-up!' Granny has snuck up behind us. 'An' if you don't roll that lip up,' Granny says, flicking me with a tea towel, 'yer gonna trip over it.' I roll my lip up, but Granny says, 'An' you and Jan feed the chooks and collect the eggs in the mornings too—less youse wanna turn at emptin' pee pots?'

'But they're not *men*!' I protest to Betty when the mean old bat is gone. 'They're boys on holiday, just like us girls!'

Betty sticks her thumb against the tack and the roster is official.

I want to discuss the unfair bits, but no one is listening.

At Granny's, Monday is wash day and Tuesday is ironing day—it's the law—but at least Granny's got a kero iron now; Granny's old Potts irons are doorstops now.

'Why don't ya get a washin' machine, Grandma?'

'No machine gonna get sheets clean, not like my ol' boiler.' It's the law!

All right for Grandma wanting to wash sheets every week, but us kids came out here for a holiday. Us kids came out here to go mustering and branding and dipping cattle with the men. Us kids didn't come out here to be washing up and washing sheets!

Granny's at her boiler and she's got Alison, Jan and me slaving at the big cement rinse tubs. Granny's boiler is a slab of cement high as my waist with a copper tub in the middle; there's a hole in the laundry wall out back, comes in under the boiler. It's the law the fire be lit under the boiler first thing Monday morning so the water is fairly bubbling while Grandma stirs the clothes with a long ironbark poker, her glasses all fogged up and sweat dripping from her nose.

It's nearly smoko time and we've *nearly* finished the small stuff. Betty and Judith helped with the big stuff, and Jackie kept the dogs away from Granny's big cane basket while they hung out twelve white sheets and the big clothes. Granny's main clothesline is long wires on a wooden T, propped up in the middle by lancewood forks; it's out there in the dog yard, but smalls get hung up in here on the veranda because the men might get struck blind or go berserk if they see Granny's underpants and big bras flapping in the breeze.

Grandma lifts the clothes from the boiler with the poker and puts them, still steaming, in Alison's tub *fer the first rinse*, Jan's tub *fer the second rinse*, and I'm at the *blue makes 'em white* tub. Alison and Jan finish their tubs, smirk at me and run out to catch their horses; they're *gonna catch up with the men an' help bring the cattle into the yards*, but I still got half a tub to do, and Granny hasn't even got a mangle.

'Be still!' Granny says real quiet.

Granny looks real mean, so I roll my lip up before I say, 'What?'

Real quiet and slow, Granny's taking the snake-catcher down off the wall.

'Don't move!' Granny says real quiet.

Move?

Real quiet and slow, Granny's getting down the old cane knife.

'Grandma?' Granny's got the cane knife above her head. 'Grandma!'

Granny lunges; the snake-catcher goes *clang* against the corrugated tin wall under the tubs. 'Gotcha!' says Granny, and clangs the cane knife down on cement. Granny holds up the snake-catcher and admires the gaping mouth and flicking tongue. 'Meet Old Joe Blake,' says Granny, and pokes the stick at me.

I'm moving now—mostly up and down—trying not to step on the long brown bit looping and buckling at my feet. I don't wanna meet old Joe Blake, so Granny says, 'I'll put this bit in the fire. You take the rest of 'im out to the dogs.'

My bit's still looping like it don't wanna get taken to the dogs. 'Grandma!'

'You heard me,' says Granny. 'Not like he's gonna bite ya!'

I look at Granny and her snake's head, and Granny looks at me. Granny doesn't say a word but I hear her loud and clear: *Alison'd do it; Jan'd do it.* I grab Joe Blake's tail end and run through the kitchen, but I'm making a whiney sound no bushie's supposed to make. Even with my hand held up high the snake is flapping and slapping on cement.

Outside, I fling it hard as I can at the dog-yard fence. It hits the wire, falls back inside.

Rover and Boxer hear me whining; they rush up to the fence and start whining too.

Boxer says, *What's happenin', Dad? What's happenin'?*

Rover says to me, *You, kid! What's all the fuss about?*

Joe Blake loops slowly.

It's a snake! Boxer bounds up and down. *It's a snake, Dad!*

Don't go near the head! Rover growls. *Remember what happened to yer mother!*

It's got no head, Dad! It's got no head! Can I 'ave it? Can I?

The dogs stand, cocked-head, at the fence and ask me, *Can we have it?*

Rover scowls. *Kids! Here, let me do it. Get outta the way, son!*

Rover's on his belly, straining his shoulder against the mesh, his leg stretched out and his paw tap-scratching at the lawn.

Boxer's got his bum in the air, tail wagging. *Can ya get it, Dad? Can ya?*

Can't ... quite ... reach ... it, son!

Here, Dad, let me hav'a go!

I kick it closer, and Rover snares the thick end with a paw. *I got 'im, son!*

I got 'im, Dad!

Both dogs pull back, threading Joe Blake through the mesh till he's stretched taut against a wire. Snarling and straining, heads death-kill flicking, they tug-of-war old Joe Blake until old Joe Blake snaps. The dogs are delighted; they rush off, tails wagging, heads held high, snake bits trailing in the dirt.

Granny's delighted too. She's standing at the kitchen door like Satan with a snake head on her pitchfork. Granny's laughing so hard her big breasts and belly are shaking.

I hate brown snakes, red dogs and Granny—and not necessarily in that order.

But I love Danny, and I love Greg too—probably in that order.

I love Danny straight away when I see him standing at Granny's dog-yard fence with red reindeer antlers on his head. I'm ten and don't believe in Santa when he finally brings me a piebald pony with big brown eyes, just like I ordered for the last five years. I love Danny, but Jan reckons her mum reckons my mum *don't know much about horses.* Jan reckons Uncle Owen reckons my mum's *real stupid,* buying a nine-year-old unbroken pony for a *kid only just learned how to ride.* Jan reckons Granny reckons *ridin' round on old Ratty's not the same as ridin' round on a green-broke colt.* I could be cranky with them, but Greg's gonna teach me everything he learned chasing clean-skin scrubbers and throwing wild bulls in the Territory—biggest cattle station in Australia—and Danny and me are *gonna prove youse all wrong!*

I love Danny straight away, but I didn't always love Greg straight away. First time Greg met Robyn was when he came in for the Easter Rodeo with the Dotswood boys, and the boys all came out to the kitchen to say g'day to Mum at her cafe. I didn't like him that day he was playing the jukebox with Robyn and bought me a Coke and I told him, *No, thank you, I don't like Coke*, and I try not to think too much about how it was Greg holding that net for my dad that day Dad went after the cats at the cafe. First time Greg came to take Robyn out, she had a new dress made by Mrs Spring and spent all day with her hair in curlers. Betty and me are gawking through the louvres when Greg pulled up out the front of our new home on Hodgkinson Street in his old green ute. He put on his new Akubra, came on up the drive to meet the family, and Robyn said, 'Take that stupid hat off!'

Robyn and Greg are going out now, and everybody loves Greg in our family; even Granny loves Greg. I reckon Greg and Granny *got on real well, right from the get go*, because Greg knows everything about horses and cattle just like my Granddad Dick. And Greg only ever wanted to work with horses and cattle in the bush, just like Granddad Dick. Greg left school and went to work on Alexandria Downs on the Barkly Tableland in the Territory; at only sixteen Greg was throwing bulls and mustering clean-skin mickeys for NAPCO, Northern Australian Pastoral Company, for eleven dollars a week on the biggest cattle station in Australia—some say biggest in the world! So the only thing Robyn doesn't like about Greg is his big Akubra hat.

*

Fletcherview: September 1944

He wore a tan fedora, and he wore it well: crown with tear-drop dent, back brim snapped up, front brim snapped down, eyes focused on the winding track ahead, and Al Jolson spinning on the turntable in his mind—'You made me love you ...'

They'd spent a sparkling, sun-drenched day at the Big Rocks. There'd been soldiers and town girls fishing and swimming and messing about in boats—and Olive May Chapman in her new swimsuit. Then, for no apparent reason, she'd taken herself up to sit in the shade of the paperbarks, taking the sparkle with her. Now here they were, pulled up at the homestead, her arms folded, nose burnt, lips a thin line, and not a word between them.

Girls, Fred decided, were mysterious creatures. Growing up, he'd never entertained the idea of girls: he couldn't talk to girls, and when he did he usually found they had nothing to say. Then a kiss and a smack at Spargo's gate had dropped a burning question on his plate: a woodcutter and a squatter's daughter?

For a couple not allowed to date—*until I turn eighteen*—they'd been seeing a lot of each other since Spargo's gate: follies, circus, cinema and lots of swimming and fishing and messing about in boats, but always with at least one sister—and burning question—in tow.

June, the sister in question this afternoon, gave him a knowing grin, climbed over Olive's knees and jumped from the Chev, leaving them in silence.

Her silence confounded him: burning questions were better left unspoken—at least until she turned eighteen.

His silence wounded her. She'd worn her new swimming costume: dove grey with bold black stripes, prettiest she could find in Charters Towers, cost half a pig, and he hadn't even noticed. *He'd* been busy noticing Noreen and Doreen Parsons splashing him and giggling: 'See you next week, Fred?' Seven more months until she turned eighteen, seven more months of every flashy Noreen and Doreen in the country flashing smiles and long tanned legs and splashing him and giggling, 'See you next week, Fred?'

'Guess I should be going.' He joggled the gears. 'Peggy will be waiting.'

She didn't move. He risked a glance and saw that she was crying: no sound of sobs, just tears. Girls were mysterious, and he, drawn by a mystery as elemental as the rotation of the Earth: 'Would you ... Do you think maybe ... Would you ... marry me some day?'

Olive swiped an angry fist across her tears. 'Of course I'm going to marry you!' She jumped down and slammed the door. 'I thought you knew that!'

*

Charters Towers Hospital: 1969

Exhaled groan ... indrawn whimper ... someone, somewhere, is moaning?

It's far off as yet, but coming closer: *groan* and *whimper*.

'Here, take these.'

It's night-time. I can't see her, only the dim outline of her veil. 'Come on, it will help you sleep.' Finger on my lip ... plastic cup on my chin ... swallow ... veil gone ... and the night ...

It's early morning, Mum beside the bed. 'Pammie?'

'What happened?'

'Danny fell, sweetheart, but the doctor says you're going to be all right.'

Riding home from our gymkhana ... a rush of horses cantering up behind ... Danny grabs the bit, races ... hits a culvert hidden in long grass ... earth rushes up ... tumbling red dirt, blue sky ... Mum beside me in the ambulance. *Is Danny all right?*

'Is Danny all right?'

'Danny's fine.' Mum puts a hand on my shoulder. 'Don't sit up. Doctor says you're to lie very still until he gets the X-rays back.'

Doctor comes and holds X-rays against the window. 'Nothing to worry about, Mrs Bagnall, just cracked vertebrae.'

Doctor goes to do his rounds—doctors aren't like in good ol' Doc Ellis's day when you had a family doctor; nowadays you don't even know his name.

Before Mum goes to open her cafe, I make her promise she won't sell Danny because it wasn't Danny's fault I cracked my back because it was me sent him mad. Granny's always saying, 'Now don't you kids go racin'! Racin' sends 'em mad!' but up in top paddock, up near Jimmy Grubb's place, is a mile of road that's flat and straight. Jan has her own pony, Silvie, and Alison's got Florin; when I was still sharing Rat-Bag with the other kids, I didn't like racing—*Granny says we're not allowed to race!*—because Ratty farts all the way and comes last because he's seventeen and a little pony.

First time I'm riding Danny, Alison and Jan say, 'Let's race!' I say, 'Granny says we're not allowed to race!' But Danny grabs the bit, and I can't believe he's catching them! Danny might be littler than the other horses, but he's built like a racehorse and can run like one too.

'Come on, let's race!' I say. 'Danny can whoop yer asses!'

That's why it wasn't Danny's fault I cracked my back when other kids cantered up behind him, just like it wasn't Danny's fault I broke my arm last year.

We're up in the cattle yards playing Indians. We're bareback and use baling twine for bridles and the cattle yards got years and years of soft grey cattle dirt so it won't hurt when you fall off. We start by walking through the stock gates and practise catching the big rail overhead and hang there like the Lone Ranger and Tonto when they let their horses keep going as decoys as someone's chasing them. Walking and trotting are okay, but when I canter Danny and grab the rail, my legs swing right up in the air, my hands slip off the rail, and the cattle dirt isn't soft—knocks the wind clean out of me, and does something to my arm. Next morning at breakfast I'm still nursing my arm so Granny grabs it. 'Give us a look at it!' I yelp when Granny grabs my arm, but Granny says, 'Ain't broke,' and gives me my arm back. Other kids think I'm a girl when I go into town with Granny next Friday morning still nursing my arm.

Fair dinkum, I could've kissed the doctor cutting off my gold bangle!

At three o'clock I'm standing on the footpath waiting for Granny. I climb into the front with her and wait for Granny to say something about the plaster cast on my arm. But she doesn't. We get loaded up at Bartlams and we're past the cemetery where the road is bitumen now when I say, 'I got a green-stick fracture, Grandma.'

Granny says, 'Told ya it wasn't broke.'

It's kind of funny thinking I'm in the same hospital as my Grand-dad Dick when he broke his leg; but he didn't just break his leg, he smashed his leg good and proper.

Mum's asked her best friend Betty Philipson to look after the cafe so she can look after me while I can't walk and can't stand up from my low bed with boards under the mattress. Says she's happy to have some time to start her scrapbook she's been gonna do for twenty years. Mum's got a biscuit tin full of old black-and-white photos other people gave her because she lost all her photo albums in the big flood. And there are newspaper clippings too. There's one about my Granddad Dick. It's only a tiny newspaper column, not even three inches long. For the man that he was, and all the things that he did, I think Dick Chapman was worth more than a three-inch column.

*

Fletcherview: October 1945

Fred draped an arm out the window and scratched Peggy behind the ear. Last ride on the running board for Peggy. In May Chapman's pigpens, Peggy would learn she was a pig, not a person. He was going to miss her: she swam with him morning and evening—swam circles squealing blue murder when he duck-dived and disappeared;

went with him from tree to tree and dropped in the shade while he chopped wood; kept her own toilet well away from the camp; never presumed to enter the tent—slept outside, her head on his feet. Every Monday morning, she'd be out beside the road waiting for him, hitch a ride on the running board as he drove back to camp; every Friday afternoon, she used to canter, squealing, behind the Chev—only gave up when he reached the main road and picked up speed.

Peggy understood Mondays' comings and Fridays' goings, but Peggy didn't understand long weekends. Returning one Tuesday morning, Fred had been vaguely disturbed when she wasn't at the road to meet him. At the camp, he couldn't punish her: she'd been crazy overcome with joy to see him—squealed and snuffled, and danced a jig as he inspected the evidence of her distress: flour and sugar bag torn open; swag rutted up and slept on.

Fred, pulling up in front of the homestead, was wondering why Olive wasn't about to meet him, when he saw her in the far corner of the dog yard, her attention so focused she hadn't heard or seen him coming.

He was hoping May Chapman's pigpens might afford them a moment alone, now that they were *officially* a dating couple: Dick had *officially* given his approval at Olive's eighteenth birthday party—where Fred had *never been so embarrassed* in all his life, sitting at the head of the table between Olive and her best friend, Betty Philipson. He'd spent the last few weekends camped at the anabranch cutting gidgee—fourpence a post—for Dick Chapman, and tonight the Chapmans were *officially* coming to town to meet Emily and George Bagnall over an *official* dinner at the Park Hotel— licensees: Bert and Vi Bagnall. Even now, Emily and Vi were setting up the dining room—*special, for Freddie an' his girl.* Fred would dearly love to dispense with formalities, but ...

... suddenly, Olive turned and came running: '*Muumm!*'

Fred saw May come to the front gate; saw mother and daughter shade their eyes and look into the distance: three riders coming at a clipping pace, trotting—but the sort of pace you put a horse at to cover long distances without tiring.

Not three riders, only two: third horse was being led …

To Fred, climbing out of the Chev, that may have meant something—may have meant nothing at all—but the attitude of the two women said something was wrong.

Slowly, he walked over, waited at a respectful distance as the two men dismounted.

'May …' Joe Downey took off his hat. His teeth caught his lip. He looked at the horizon: 'I'm so sorry, May.'

Two men caught May Chapman as she slumped.

Olive cried in Fred's arms.

In Loving Memory of
My dear husband and our father,
Edwin Richard Chapman
Accidentally killed October 29th, 1945
Aged 44
At Rest

*

Townsville Daily Bulletin: **Thursday, 1 November 1945**

BUSH FATALITY NEAR MINGELA

A fatal accident occurred at Marlow Station, via Mingela, on Monday morning. Mr. Edwin Richard Chapman, 44, married, with a wife and four children residing at Fletcherview Station, was fatally injured on his property, Marlow Station, at about 7.30 am. At the time of the accident Mr. Chapman was felling a tree for the purpose of splitting posts. The tree, when falling, struck the limb of a dry tree 35 feet up, breaking off the limb which struck Mr. Chapman. His brother, Mr. Robert James Chapman, who was assisting him, went to Quilp's outstation of Dotswood, where he contacted Dotswood by telephone. The Charters Towers ambulance and the Mingela police were advised, and Superintendent R. Bartlett, of the ambulance, on arrival at the scene found Chapman was dead. There were abrasions on his scalp and he had been haemorrhaging from the nostrils. The police took charge of the body and accompanied the ambulance to Charters Towers. Mr. Chapman seems to have been dogged by misfortune: he had only just recovered from a badly broken leg. Mr. Chapman was highly regarded as a horse and cattleman and was a member of a highly respected family. Deep sympathy is extended to his widow and children.

*

Mum's scrapbook:

His birthday was on the 24th of October, he was 44 years old. On the 29th he was killed on Marlow, our new property. The hardest part to bear was when the men brought the horses home. Dad's horse had a saddle on—but no Dad.

7

It never rains but it pours ...

1969

1969 was a bad year.

At 4.30 am Granny's grumbling in the kitchen, and the Blitz is grumbling at the dog-yard gate. The Blitz is Granny's old army truck left over by the Yanks; there are two sugar-bag seats in the battered metal cab, and two permanent dents on top of the cab made by little kids sitting up there. Those dents were made by Robyn and Jennifer, Betty and Judith, Richard and David, then Jan and me. Tony and John are up there sitting in our dents because we're big enough to ride on the big mudguard humps over the front wheels—Jan on one side and me on the other. Windscreen doesn't have glass, so we hang on to the frame as Richie puts *'er into gear* and the Blitz bumps across the road. Richard's thirteen (some people call him Dick, but it never really stuck) and Uncle Ian's teaching him to drive because kids *gotta learn to drive in the bush*. Uncle Ian with sticky-out eyebrows is head stockman now, and Mum's big sister Aunty Dulcie is Granny's cook because Jan's mum and dad are back on their feet at their shop in town. Jan's twelve and can drive since her dad taught her last year; only I can't drive.

The cows hear the Blitz coming and come running. They follow us, bawling loudly all the way up to two big hay sheds up there on the high ground where Granny was gonna shift the house one day but then a Widow Maker killed Granddad Dick before he got round to it. Those big sheds started out full of lucerne—they're not full now—and if the drought doesn't break soon even Granny Chapman's gonna be in trouble. Granny's already given *her bullocks away fer two bob*, and Granny's had to bring her breeders close to home for feeding. Granny's cows are starving poor; Granny's cows are red hide and bone.

In the shed, Richard and Alison climb the tiers of hay and throw down bales, and Uncle Ian stacks them on the big open back of the Blitz. 'C'monnn! C'mon, c'mon!' Everyone calls the cows but you don't have to call the cows; cows are bawlin' and jostlin' and trottin' along behind, and us kids cut the bales and throw out slices of lucerne before heading back for our breakfast.

The cows Granny moved close to home brought their flies with them. You can't eat your steak and eggs without swallowing a fly, or maybe gagging on one. Up there, dangling in the Christmas decorations, are long yellow strips of sticky tape that Granny's hung up; they're dotted with dead flies and flies still buzzing in the glue. Granny's got flycatchers hanging in the kitchen too.

Uncle Ian and the boys are going over to Pandanus to check the mill and cut scrub for cattle to eat. Alison, Jan and me have our job: *You girls do the washin'-up before youse disappear.* After, we ride along Lolworth and the Burdekin, checking waterholes, because sometimes cattle get bogged in the mud and they're too weak to pull themselves out. When we find one, the men come with the Toyota and pull it out.

One time at the Dead Hole over at the Big Rocks, we found a cow bogged halfway up her belly. Crows had already pecked her eyes out, and maggots were eating at her bum where manure had piled up. If I had a gun, I could've shot that cow right there and then, but we had to ride home and get the men to come and shoot her. We never did find Rat-Bag. When the men ran the horses in this year, Ratty wasn't with them. Us kids rode all down Lolworth, down Big Sandy and back up along the Burdekin. We found one of Granny's big Hereford bulls smashed on the rocks at the bottom of a basalt cliff. Everyone came and had a look. Figured he must've been brawling with another bull up there on top of that black cliff and got pushed over. We rode and rode but couldn't find Ratty. I couldn't have shot Ratty, but I'd let the men shoot him. No one should die alone like that.

As if dingoes mauling calves and cows dying all over the place with crows pecking their eyes isn't enough, Granny's got rubber vine. Rubber vine has glossy dark-green leaves and white and purple flowers, and grows as much as five yards in a month and scrambles up native trees and strangles them. During the war some men planted the rubber vine deliberate because after the fall of Singapore they were gonna make our own rubber in Australia but never got round to it. Now some parts along Lolworth, cattle can't get down to drink; wild pigs hide under the tangles and you can't muster cattle through rubber vine. And it can kill a horse or cow because they eat it when there's no grass. Those men who planted rubber vine were probably no more stupid than those men brought in cane toads to eat cane beetles the cane toads couldn't even reach, or those men brought in rabbits and foxes for hunting. No more stupid than those men putting young boys' numbers in a barrel and pulling them out to say which boys go to Vietnam. Greg's best mate John Costello, whose family owns Fanning Downs, he was pulled out of the barrel. Everybody's thanking God Greg didn't get pulled out of the barrel and sent to Vietnam because Robyn and Greg are engaged now.

When we get home Granny's at the front gate sucking her teeth and looking at the sky: sky's ochre-orange to the west, silver blue to the east; ground's shimmering in heatwaves. We're all parched, tonguing for a drink. 'Youse kids take care of yer horses first!' We unsaddle, run out to the back veranda where Granny keeps two canvas water bags hanging from the upstairs landing, fight over the pannikin and drink and drink and drink.

Toyota's coming in. Richard in the back with a calf between his legs.

Richard tells how that little calf's mother was eating a bone and got it stuck halfway down her neck—*could see it stickin' out both sides*—tells how they ran the cow down easy she was so weak, wrapped her tail around a tree and Uncle Ian held her horns and Richard pulled the bone out, but she'd been too long so they shot her anyway.

We've got *six* poddies to bottle-feed before tea.

'Come on, youse girls.' Granny's crotchety these days. We wash our feet in a washtub outside the bathroom. Men get a turn at the shower, and you can hear them blowing dust out of their noses, but Granny and us girls shower together. Granny's bathroom is corrugated tin, cement floor and really big; you could hold a dance in Granny's bathroom—or soap up the floor and slide around when there's plenty of water in Granny's tanks. These days us girls stand in the big bathtub and Granny runs two inches of water in the bottom. We soap up then Granny turns the shower on us one at a time: 'Front, back. Git out!' Just like running cattle through a dip.

Granny takes her glasses off, puts them on the shelf. Granny's got a turkey neck and a face that looks funny without glasses. Granny pulls her dress over her head, says, 'Give us a hand, would'ja?' I grab the hem and give it a tug. Granny Chapman might wear dresses, but everyone knows who wears the pants at Fletcherview. Granny's always saying *You kids gonna git a taste of the stockwhip,* but only one time Granny ever meant it was when she found two nail holes punched in the wall—that wall there, between the bathroom and the toilet. Granny took after David and Richard with her stockwhip that one time. Granny couldn't catch 'em, but us girls wished she did because *You boys shoulda got what youse had comin'!*

Granny's bra is as big as my head; when she takes her bra off her big titties hang down on her belly. Granny's like a sumo; her belly's big enough a fully cooked baby could fit in there. Granny soaps up in our dirty water, picks up her titties one at a time to wash under them, and I'm thinking, *Why do old people let themselves get like that?*

Granny catches me gawking, says, 'Can't make a silk purse out of a sow's ear.'

After tea, we play cards for a bit. 'Why dontcha get a TV, Grandma?'

'Got no electric, ya dozy gits!'

'Well, why don't she get some?'

Granny won't even let us listen to her wireless; except for the news, Granny *don't wanna go wastin' batteries.*

I'm in a big double bed with Jan. We sleep together at Granny's. And we're blood brothers now. We cut our thumbs with a razor blade and mixed our blood together like Indians. We're reading *My Friend Flicka* when Granny yells, 'You girls turn that lamp off!'

No ceiling at Granny's, so Granny can see our light and we can see Granny's shadow up there on the roof. 'Not even eight o'clock, Grandma!'

'Lamps out! Big day tomorrow!'

We're all sunburnt—*topped a hundred and ten agin t'day!*—and hot and bothered—*dontcha wish Granny'd get some fans?*—and dog-tired, so I lower the wick and blow out the lamp.

Other kids laugh when I kneel beside the bed, so at Granny's I pray lying down: If Your purpose, God, is that all Your creatures should reach heaven one day and if You have all this power like they say, why don't You simply order, *Go on, git on up to heaven!* That's what my Granny Chapman would do if Granny was God. Granny wouldn't muck about. Granny'd crack her stockwhip: *Up to heaven with the lot of yers, right now! David 'n' Ritchie, youse git on down to hell where youse headin' anyway!*

And, God, look out for Rat-Bag and Emily Bagnall, who just died. I think you might have let us find Ratty, and I think you might have let our Grandma Bag hang around till Christmas so Dad didn't have to bury his mum on Christmas Eve.

Granny's lamp goes out; the house creaks in darkness; the roof pops and cracks.

Big day tomorrow: tomorrow at four thirty, we'll do it all again.

But God help Granny Chapman if the drought don't break soon ...

*

Christmas 1971

On Christmas Eve, 1971, at 10 am EST, severe tropical cyclone Althea crossed the coast some 50 km north of Townsville. Wind gusts to 196 km/h (106 knots) were recorded at Townsville at 0830 EST, and torrential rain ...

Cyclone Althea stopped the Hamiltons coming up from Townsville, and *almost* stopped us Bagnalls having Christmas Day with Granny Chapman. 'Why won't Grandma get the phone on?' Granny used to have a party line, but now the exchange has gone automatic Granny doesn't even have a party line. We can't even let Granny know we're gonna try an' make it out to Fletcherview. Alloways and Grahams aren't even gonna try.

Little Sandy was running a banker but only a foot over the bridge so we made it across and got as far as Big Sandy. Big Sandy's over the bridge; water's brown and frothy but only a bit of current in the middle. *She's starting to back up!* That means Big Burdekin just down there must be running a banker too.

Billy Grubb's sitting on the bank in drizzling rain looking to get across. Billy's brother, Jimmy Grubb, lives up the road at Fletcherdale, but Billy Grubb's an ol' batchla lives just outside Charters Towers. Billy hitches a ride to town every Friday. You see him up the street in gabardine riding pants and R.M. Williams high-heeled riding boots. Billy Grubb's always got a half-smoked roly in one corner of his mouth, dribble of spit hanging from his chin and damp patch on his shirt. My middle sister, Betty, says Billy Grubb's always wanting to talk to the office girls at Bartlams Ltd, where she works, and at Christmas, Billy chases them. Betty says Christmas or not, she *still don't wanna kiss 'im.*

Billy comes over, says something, might be *Merry Christmas*, and: 'Was gonna hoof it up t' Jimmy's place fer Christmas.'

Billy Grubb's hard to understand. Almost no one can understand Billy Grubb.

Billy Grubb's carrying a hessian sack—could be a dead cat he's got in there. Maybe kittens he's gonna drown? Or a human head! I stand on the other side of Mum when Billy comes over because I'm too big to hold her hand.

Dad and Greg walk the bridge but it's *too deep to risk it!* Our Volksie can't make it; even Greg's ute, with all us sitting in the back, can't make it. Looks like we're not gonna make it out to Granny's for Christmas dinner this year. Only, Mum's *not about to let Grandma spend Christmas on her own*, so Dad gets the blow-up dinghy out of the boot. By the time Dad and Greg get it pumped up, we see

Granny's old grey Land Rover coming down the far bank. Granny gets out, cups her hands around her mouth. 'Just come lookin' to see if yers were gonna try an' make it!'

'We're gonna make it, Granny!'

Greg picks me up, dumps me in the dinghy, starts dragging me across. It's a long way, maybe eighty yards of brown water. Betty's walking beside us. Betty gets thigh-deep and Betty disappears. 'Dozy git's gone and stepped off the edge of the bridge!' Her head bobs up, and in a whisker Betty's head's fifty yards downstream, one hand holding her book *King of Oil* above her head. 'Don't fight it! Keep your lungs full! Go with the flow!' If Betty uses so much as her big toe to fight the current, she'll go under. We watch, but we're not *real* worried: current's not *real* strong and it's already angling her towards still water along the far bank. All us kids know how to shoot rapids and ride floodwaters: done it a hundred times playing down at Lolworth and over at the Big Rocks.

Billy Grubb can't swim. Greg has to ferry Billy and his sack across in the dinghy before Greg goes back and gets my big sister Robyn. Greg and Robyn's wedding was the best ever! First time anyone's seen Dad a bit tiddly drinking champagne, but when Mum and Robyn tease him, Dad goes red and says he wasn't. Dad says he did *not* put his suit coat over his head and cluck like a chicken. He did, because Mum got a bit cranky when she did the Pride of Erin with Uncle Ian and the Gypsy Tap with Uncle Owen, because Dad won't dance in public and Mum told Dad he was chicken so Dad put his coat over his head and clucked like one.

Dad's holding Mum's hand and his mango as they wade across— only not Granny's cement pot because they can't carry it—and we all wait for Betty. She comes trudging up the bank covered in brown silt and has mud up to her knees but *King of Oil* is mostly dry. Dad gives Granny her special mango, and Mum and Dad sit in the front with her; we climb into the back, and Billy Grubb's gonna climb in too! *Personally*, I reckon we oughta let Billy hoof it up to Jimmy's. Jimmy Grubb's is only five mile up there, just past Granny's, where we race our horses on the road.

Billy sits beside me, puts his sack between his boots, *chink, chink, chink, chink*.

Billy sees me looking at his sack. He opens it, shows me six long-neck brown bottles and a piece of uncooked corned meat coated with little bits of hessian; dribble on Billy's chin drips into the sack and Billy gives me a nod that says, *Billy Grubb don't come empty-handed; not on Christmas Day, he don't.*

I'm glad it's not a human head in his sack, and years later I'm sad when Billy Grubb is diagnosed with tongue cancer; when they cut out half of Billy's tongue no one can understand him.

Anyway, when we get up to Fletcherview Granny's really cranky: there's no brandy for the custard and no sherry for the plum pudding!

Granny's got a new cook. And the new cook drank it.

*

The Cairns Post: Monday, 4 March 1946

STOP PRESS! DISASTER FEARED IN BURDEKIN AREA

BRISBANE, MARCH 3—The greatest cyclonic floods in Queensland's history are devastating 446 miles of the coastal belt between Mackay and Cairns. Millions of tons of flood water from the rain-soaked northern catchment areas are rushing down the Burdekin River. Home Hill, Giru and Ayr, and the entire Lower Burdekin district, face disaster.

At 8 o'clock to-night the Burdekin River was 78 feet 6 inches at Selheim ... This is almost 15 feet above the previous record of 63 feet 10 inches in 1927 ...

A disaster of unforeseeable magnitude was only escaped this afternoon when the cyclone re-crossed the coast off Mackay and headed out to sea before it could flood the southern catchment area of the Burdekin. The entire area has been blackened out as all communications are severed.

Far to the north of Fletcherview Homestead, a raging Burdekin River was thundering from the mountains at Hells Gates. Two mile lower, a swollen Douglas joined the torrent from the east. Eight mile lower, Oakey Creek had been stalled at its junction; less than a mile further down, Running River—a tributary draining nearly 300 square mile of country in the Mount Spec area—was beginning to back up.

Further down, below Starbright Station, three more tributaries already stood stalled at their junctions. The Star River, whose flood-waters came from the high rainfall area beyond Paluma, had broken its banks; eight mile below the Star, Basalt River—1100 square mile of watershed—had broken too; six mile lower, Keelbottom Creek—620 square mile of watershed—was running backwards.

And the Burdekin thundered on.

Lower still—in May Chapman's 'back yard'—the Fletcher, Lolworth and Big Sandy creeks were already running bankers ...

For May Chapman, dawn had been a long time coming.

May put her ear to the wireless, ran the dial up and down: Static! Static! Static!

'Don't just stand there, youse girls! Go check the marker in the gully like I told yers!'

May tried the party line: two long, one short for Hillgrove—nothing.

May tried Jimmy Grubb at Fletcherdale: one long, two short—nothing.

May drummed her fingers on the redwood table: wireless and party line down; news last night said six inches fell above Fletcherview; gale-force winds and heavy rain all night, still raining now.

Move! May Chapman knew God helps them that help themselves, but May Chapman couldn't move. May Chapman felt swamped already: only two girls home, and old Percy.

Oh, Dick!

'Jimmy Grubb's out front!' Olive panted, dripping at the door.

'Git that dog outside, Ollie!' May took a swipe. 'Trackin' mud in everywhere!'

Mitzie, bright-eyed with excitement, had a shake: *See, all dry now!* Melva, bright-eyed with excitement, caught the terrier and ran outside. 'Goin' back to watch water comin' up!'

'Jimmy says come up to his place,' Olive relayed breathlessly. 'Says stations further up all got out last night! Says Burdekin's comin' down ...'

'Tell him we're stayin' put!'

'Already told him. Says he won't take no for an answer.'

From the veranda, May took in sheets of water—both sides of the road; she took in Jimmy Grubb hunched in the saddle, rain streaming from his hat. Jimmy's horse, tail turned to the wind, was fetlock deep in water.

May Chapman sucked her teeth. *Still water: backup water.*

May yelled above the drumming rain. Jimmy yelled back. Wind snatched their words, carried them away. Jimmy waved up towards his place; May pointed at her upstairs landing.

'Could take the Buick.' Percy had come out onto the veranda. 'Could drive up ...'

'Bog before we get outta the shed! Why'd ya think Jimmy come on his horse?'

'All right! All right!' old Percy turned his back to the wind.

'No need to take me head off.' Percy cupped his hands, struck a match and sucked on his pipe. 'Just sayin' is all.'

Puffing blue smoke, he flicked the match into water lapping at the veranda.

And, even as they watched, a first trickle snaked its way across the cement.

The old bookkeeper caught Olive's eye. 'What'd you reckon, Ollie?'

'Gully's already come up six foot past the marker we put down this morning, Mum.'

'An' if yer'd not spent all day down there gawpin', yer'd have some bakin' done!' May Chapman was on the move: *Ollie, git this; Melva, that. Won't come higher than the table.*

Percy sidestepped the activity. Percy was *too old to be shiftin' sugar sacks; too old to be cartin' flour bags ...*

The redwood table was stacked high with dry goods; storeroom was nearly empty. May and Melva were trying to heft the Singer when Percy cleared his throat. 'Mrs Chapman.'

The veranda was ankle deep, and, even as they watched, a first trickle found its way into the dining room. 'Don't just stand there lookin', Ollie! Go git them goats and pigs up across the road. Git a move on! Melva, help me up with this.'

Outside, the sky was grey; the world was grey; the wind came in angry bursts.

Olive dipped her head and ran into the rain. She splashed up through the house yard, thanked God the dogs were over at Southern View with Dulcie and Bill Whalen—dog kennels were already under.

She waded through the hollow in the night horse paddock. Goat and pigpens were an island—*still water: backup water*—the animals milling restlessly. She drove the pigs out first, drove them down towards the house, but they baulked at the channel beside the road and began to circle back. Olive coaxed Peggy—*only need one pig to lead them ... Peggy loves swimming ...* She had to save Peggy!

But Peggy was a pig now, not a person. Peggy circled back.

Olive found a stick; the pigs swam out, circled back. Olive hit, kicked, yelled and cursed. Pigs were going nowhere. Pigs wanted the safety of their island pen.

Goats were worse: they bleated pitifully, backing into the driving rain.

'Leave 'em!' May came wading knee deep through the house yard. 'Leave 'em!' she yelled, waving chaff bags. 'Get my turkeys!' Three turkeys to a bag, mother and daughter crossed the road, released the birds, turned back for another load and—

And the world stood still.

The world stood still because it was moving: the breakaway gully to the east of the homestead was a torrent; up beyond the house, petrol drums were being floated from the shed. *That's* not backup water. *That's* Burdekin water. The river had broken its banks.

'Gonna shut the doors!' Olive was wading up towards the sheds.

'Git back here, Ollie!'

Olive wrestled with the big, heavy doors; water was only knee deep at the sheds, but the drag of current defeated her.

'Git back here, ya stupid bugger!'

Olive gave up, and looked back: the house was moored in a moving plane of water; the hollow she'd waded through, moments before, fast flowing. She knew she had to get upstream: high enough to let the current sweep her down to the house. She waded; she stopped to judge width and strength, but her mum waved her higher. She waded further, took a breath. Current snared her, carried her away. *Don't fight it! Keep your lungs full! Go with the flow!* Olive had swum the Burdekin—*done it a hundred times*—but running water isn't floodwater: *no buoyancy in floodwater; turbulent water sucks you down; turgid water offers no resistance; stroking arms and hands aren't fast enough to catch rushing water*. Until her knees scraped ground and she pulled herself up, gasping.

Main current behind her, she fed along the fence line, one post at a time, up towards the house yard. 'You stupid girl! You stupid, stupid bugger!'

Olive had never seen May cry. Her mum didn't even cry at the funeral.

Olive started crying too.

Thigh deep, they pushed back to the veranda.

'Stop that silly cryin' now, Ollie! Cryin' won't git us nowhere.'

Percy and Melva were waiting on the fourth step; bottom three were under. 'I got Cockie!' Melva held up the cage. 'I took Mitzie up, and all the photos off the walls like you said.' Melva wasn't excited anymore: ground floor was three foot deep in moving water.

Out front, the current was already *too wide, too deep!* to try for the high ground.

There was only one way to go: up. 'Come on, Ollie. Melva. Grab what ya can!'

Grab what? Rational minds refused to work in an irrational world. *Grab what?*

May looked up the staircase. *Fifteen steps up to the second floor, eleven dry steps now.* May took one last look at the dining room. Water was lipping the dry goods on the redwood table; flour had a water stain creeping up the side. Her mother's pianola ... Singer ... her Dad's kerosene fridge ... sideboard ... rosewood chiffonier ... wedding presents ... odds and ends, bits and pieces of a life ... flotsam, jetsam ...

Oh, Dick!

May said goodbye to the dining room. Ten dry steps now.

Upstairs, Olive was looking from a casement window. No island up there now, just a handful of goats, stranded on the pigpen roof; pigs weren't so nimble. Unreal world: water was spilling animals over the fence; kids already drowned; goats, swimming, surrendering, were whirled away, sucked under.

May sat on the bed, bed where Ollie was born. *Look out for your daughters, Dick. Please, look out for your girls.*

In silence, they recorded the rising water in steps: only seven dry steps now.

Six steps. Olive took her treasures from her glory box.

'Start to go down now, Ollie,' May said. 'So much water can't keep on risin'.'

Five steps. Olive wrapped her treasures in her Driza-Bone. Tied it: *tight! tight! tight!*

Two steps. Olive shoved her Driza-Bone into Cockie's cage.

Cockie spiked his yellow comb, screeching protest: *C'mon, Mitzie; c'mere, Mitzie!*

Midday: no steps left to count; floorboards beneath their feet were darkening.

'Told ya we should go up to Grubb's,' Percy muttered to no one in particular.

'An' I told you, Granddad come up here in '27.' May was taking picture frames from the floor, and stacking them on beds. 'Water only come up to his knees up here in '27.'

Water around her ankles, May started throwing *me best linen up there* onto the valances. *Granddad stayed up here all one night an' half next day, in '27. Water only come up to his knees up here in '27.*

2 pm: Water was lapping at the mattresses. 'Gonna go higher than '27, Mum.'

3 pm: Water, inside and out, was spilling through the windows. 'This much water just can't keep on risin'. Start to go down soon.'

3.05 pm: Olive was judging the casement windows—and her mother. 'Mum?'

'Can't keep on risin', Ollie.'

'Already higher than '27, Mum.'

3.10 pm: Olive moved Cockie's cage over by the window. 'Mum?'

'Prob'ly won't hafta, Ollie. Can't keep on risin'.'

3.15 pm: May pushed a window open against the tide. 'Not raining so hard now.'

May looked across at the kitchen roof—built separate for risk of fire—an arm's length away. Gap between sill and kitchen roof was a whirlpool. *Gonna have to climb out … step across to the skillion … crawl up along the kitchen roof … step from the peak back across the gap, an' onto the main roof.* 'Prob'ly won't hafta,' May said. 'But better do it while we still got some daylight. You girls go first; that way yer can givus a hand across.'

Olive pulled her eiderdown off the valance.

'Leave it! Git ruined out there; only be up there a few hours.'

Olive put a knee on the sill.

'Can't keep on risin'.'

Olive felt above her head, caught the frame outside. *Put one hand up there, Ollie …* Twisting, she straightened slowly. *Just don't look at moving water.* She was facing the house. *Make ya dizzy.* Cheek pressed against tin, she stretched one foot out behind her—*just step on straight across*—felt about, found purchase—*let go one hand now*—she was standing, legs spread between windowsill and kitchen skillion, torrent gushing across her feet.

Paused between heaven and hell, she took a breath—Olive was over.

Crouched in rain on the roof outside, Olive coaxed, 'Don't jump, Melve. Step. It's easy … don't look down … you can do it … good girl. Mitzie first … now Cockie … now you, Percy.'

Percy passed an old washtub through the window.

'What d'ya want that for?'

'You'll see!'

'Givus yer hand!'

Percy was *too old to be climbing through windows.*

'I got ya, Percy!'

Percy was *too old to be crawlin' up sloping roofs on 'is hands 'n' knees.*

'Go on, up ya go!'

Goddarn, he's too darn old.

May put a knee on a sill inches deep in water. Both hands on the frame, she hoisted herself up.

'Twist the other way, Mum! Slide forward, twist the other way. No!'

May wrested another inch from the window; her bodice snagged, tore.

'Stand up now, Mum! Turn around. Other way!'

May was reaching out to helping hands reaching out to help her. She was over!

Standing on the skillion roof, ridiculously, foolishly, they were laughing. In each other's arms, they hugged and laughed—at some outrageous joke. Their laughter died. On hands and knees they clawed up, slipped down, clawed up the sharp, sharp slant of the kitchen roof.

They sat. Legs astride the peak. And breathed.

In front, the main roof beckoned, but they had yet to recross the gap. Behind, the world was moving away: a sea of logs, upturned trees, wallabies and kangaroos and puffed-up cattle floating by, Who'd have thought ... who'd believe there was so much water in the world?

Unreal world: water without end, Amen! played havoc with the senses. It was *they* who were moving: riding the roof of an outhouse kitchen through still waters. 'Don't look at it!' they said. 'Don't look down!' they said. 'Just look up,' they said. Only stable point of reference was the house roof—just there: two foot up, three feet away. 'Keep comin'!' They clambered. 'Take my hand!' They crawled. 'One more push!' They heaved and hauled each other up onto the house roof.

Dusk.

Thump! Another bullock whirled away.

Crash! A log disappeared, was trapped—*bang! bang! bang!*—hammering the house.

Place stood up to it in '27, place'll stand up to it agin ...

Night fell; lightning showed which way heaven; water lapped at gutters. The night hosted unnamed thumps, groans, and other, more horrifying phantoms.

Dulcie and June ... tailing cattle over at Southern View ... they'll be sleeping dry tonight. Bill Whalen will look out for Dulce and June. Bill Whalen's a good man.

Rain slackened, wind fell. Percy was hunkered like a turtle, washtub over his head.

If—when—it came to it, Olive would let Cockie out of his cage. Cockie had never learned to fly; Cockie fell out of the nest; best Cockie ever did was flutter across the lawn chasing Mitzie, trying to bite his tail: *C'mon, Mitzie; c'mere, Mitzie.* Strange, how the thought of Cockie chasing Mitzie on the front lawn made Olive want to cry. She'd heard drowning is not a painful death. *Come here, Mitzie.* Olive took her Driza-Bone from Cockie's cage. Arms wrapped around it, she held her treasures to her chest: *when—if—they find her ...*

Melva was asleep, head on May's lap.

Mitzie on her lap, Olive leaned her head against her mother's shoulder. Drowsing, she catalogued her dreams: Fred, a home of their own, and babies—she wants lots and lots of babies. Please, God!

Pale clouds, briefly silvered by moon; brown water, leisurely by moonlight.

Love. May stroked wet hair from Olive's cheek. *Love can't raise the dead.*

Grief? She'd thought burying her husband would be the greatest trial she'd ever face. *Damn you, Dick Chapman!* They were going to have to spend the night up here, praying for the dawn. *Oh, Dick. Please save your daughters! Please save your girls.*

And dawn was gonna be a long time coming.

Place stood up to it in '27; place'll ...

Roof groaned, lifted, shifted ...

Oh, Dick!

*

Mum's scrapbook:

And so began the longest night of my life. How my 14 stone mother ever climbed up on that roof, she could never explain. My menagerie was then passed up, along with a photo of my dad and a bundle of love letters from my boyfriend. We huddled on that sloping roof for over 10 hours in pitch darkness and drizzling rain. And always with the constant fear of snakes ... Percy had an iron washtub over his head; the poor old dear sat all night with a 12 pack of red-head matches trying to light his pipe which wouldn't light. So in boredom he would fall asleep and the tub would crash on the iron roof and we would nearly die of fright thinking that the roof had started to give way.

At long last daylight appears and it is evident that the flood is receding and we were safe only because our pioneering ancestors built the old home to stay put. The top floor actually did lift off the iron plates on the posts and had moved a few inches sideways. The clean-up is really difficult, particularly as our water tanks were twisted wrecks half a mile downstream and the windmill lying tiredly on its side.

*

March 2013

Mum lost everything in the big flood of '46. She saved only a photo of her father, a piece of bone from his leg, and all of Dad's love letters. Come hell or high water, Mum kept every letter Dad ever wrote to her, a whole bundle of them. My sister has them.

Which sister? I hear you ask.

There's only one; I only have one sister now, but I don't want to go there just yet.

When the cyclone struck, Dad was stranded somewhere north of Ingham—road and rail cut—but as soon as he got back to Charters Towers, he went looking for his sweetheart. Seventeen mile and two flooded creeks to cross, he hitched a lift to Little Sandy, swam it and walked to Big Sandy. He swam it—going, from treetop to treetop—then he walked on up to Fletcherview.

My mother was only sixteen when they met; Dad was twenty-six. Karmic predestination? Or is 'love at first sight' just another lie we tell ourselves in order to make sense of a random world?

My father wasn't one to abrogate—delegate—responsibility.

Not to Karma. Not to God.

After sixty-five years of marriage, she was part of him: I should have known (did know?) that he could no more abandon her than he could abandon himself, and I should have known (did know?) that anguish such as his could only be erased through self-annihilation.

But I did nothing to stop it.

8

When winning feels like losing

Grade Nine, 1972

Time was, grown-ups knew things!

Time was, grown-ups taught you how to plait your hair and ride a bike. Time was, Mum kissed your forehead, *Nigh-night, love.* Time was, Dad lay on a tarp looking up at the stars and told again about his little pony and patted you when you cried for Toby, and cried for the boy too.

Big girls don't cry!

Come fourteen, grown-ups have taught everything they know—which isn't much.

I'm sitting up the mango tree in the backyard of our home in Hodgkinson Street. If you were to ask why I'm sitting up a mango tree, I'd blow smoke thoughtfully, narrow my eyes and I'd tell ya, 'Frigged if I know!'

Seemed like a good idea at the time. No one can see me up here. Not unless they stand directly underneath and look up. Not likely anyone's gonna stand directly underneath and look up: Mum's working; Dad's working; Betty's working; Robyn's working at the ANZ and moved into her new home with Greg. So it's just me, sitting up a mango tree flicking long blonde hair from my shoulder, tilting my chin aggressively, blowing smoke thoughtfully: smoking Alpine; looking Kool.

Ask me why? Just told ya: Frigged if I know. I could be working down at Mum's cafe. I don't mind peeling potatoes or washing up, but I'd rather chew glass than serve at the counter and have friggin' people gawk at me.

Time was, you could say 'frig' till the cows came home: *Why've I gotta ride me friggin' bike to school when I've got so many friggin' books?* (Same friggin' bike Robyn rode to friggin' school—coat of blue paint don't make it look friggin' new!)

Cows came home day after Mum asked Dad what 'frig' meant.

Girls at school say worse than 'frig'. Girls at Gabes say f – – k.

Mum sent me to St Gabes but I'm still going to All Souls. By the time Jan and I got to Grade Seven, Gabes was so broke all the girls were being bussed over to All Souls. Mum likes St Gabes because Mum was married in the chapel there. But Mum only went to school for two years because she didn't like exams.

I love exams. Could do exams all day. Exams aren't my problem.

Gabes is a boarding school. Only five 'day girls' at St Gabes. Jan and I are the only day girls in our class. Boarders call us Dagos. We don't care. Who needs 'em? Jan and I don't need 'em. We have our horses and each other. Grade Nine girls are stupid. Sneak around the toilets smoking cigarettes at recess. Nothing looks so stupid as girls thinking they look grown up smoking cigarettes. Only thing looks more stupid is girls pulling hair and scratching. Different if a girl could throw a proper punch, or maybe do kung-fu.

Time was, a wedgie was an eagle. Time was, I thought 'euthanasia' was 'youth in Asia'. Who gives a frig about youth in Asia? Youth in Australia got our own problems!

Betty's gotta watch *Bellbird*! *Bellbird*'s a serial.

I gotta watch *Mr Ed*! Mr Ed is dead!

We're fighting so hard over the channel knob, friggin' channel knob comes out.

'Betty broke the TV, Mum! And when Robyn stuck up for me, Betty sat on her till *Bellbird* finished!'

'Never mind, love, it's just a silly program.'

Mr Ed was euthanised. Some say it was an accident—a tranquilliser, inadvertently administered while Bamboo Harvester (that was his real name) was in retirement. Mr Ed is buried at Snodgrass Farm in Oklahoma. Mr Ed's dead two years and I didn't even know!

And now no one can watch *Mr Ed* till the man can come and fix the TV.

On her days off, Betty wears a purple nightie as a dress. She teases her hair into an afro, ties a purple strip round her forehead. Betty looks at me above a pair of John Lennon glasses perched on her nose. 'You been into my face wash again!'

'Didn't use much!'

Betty cut the letters L-O-V-E out of psychedelic wallpaper and pasted LOVE on the back of the wardrobe we shifted out from the wall between Betty's bed and mine so I *don't have to look at her stupid face!* And Betty don't *have to listen to her whine!* Betty keeps me awake at night, laughing. Monty Python isn't funny; Monty Python's just plain stupid. But Betty's not totally stupid. One time when I couldn't balance my books, Betty showed me, 'If ya put that in this column, put that in that column, it's all gotta balance. See?' If our teacher, Mr C from Swaziland, showed it like Betty showed it, anyone can balance books.

When Mum built our new house on Hodgkinson Street and Dad put down the only cement footpath in Hodgkinson Street, Mum thought it would be nice for her three girls to share one big room. Dumb! When Robyn married Greg and moved out, Mum had a man put a wall up. Betty and I have our own rooms now but Betty got the big walk-in wardrobe; I got the cupboard.

Betty plays her records so loud noise thumps the wall. When Don McLean drives his Chevy to the levee for the fifty-thousandth time, I yell, 'Wish the levee wasn't dry so maybe he'd drown in it!' Only one I like is Helen Reddy: 'I am woman'. But how do you burn your bra when you haven't got one? No point in buying a bra with nothing to put in it. And, if we're *no longer living in the era of the traditional social family structure where the man was expected to be the sole breadwinner*—and Mum gets more money at her cafe than Dad gets at the railway—how come Dad still wears the pants?

Mum drives a red Volksie since she lent Aunty Dulcie our cream Volksie and Aunty Dulcie went and rolled it. I heard Granny say, 'Typical of Ollie. If yer asked Ollie, she'd lend ya her arsehole and shit through 'er ribs.' Red Volksie has screechy brakes. One time we go out to All Souls to pick up David, but Dough-arse can't have his mates see him in a red Volksie with screechy brakes. Uncle Owen had to drive all the way into town to pick up Dough-arse in his new blue Valiant. Dad says he'd've made Dough-arse walk. At least Dad and I agreed on that.

I pretty much let Mum and Betty know I hate 'em. I'm not game to let Dad know I hate him—but I think Dad knows anyway.

'Dad, if $2x^2 + 3xy - 36 = 0$, what's x worth?'

Dad spends half an hour explaining something *useful*, like how to find the volume of water in a tank; no point in telling Dad we don't have to find the volume of water in a tank in our exam tomorrow. Dad says, 'Why don't they teach you something useful?' No point in telling Dad we don't need to know every river in Australia or list every tributary of the Burdekin. All I have to know is what x is worth! Besides, I only asked Dad what x was worth because I know Dad doesn't know what x is worth and I can do it in my head.

Busloads of primary school kids pull up at our front gate and Dad shows his rocks and how to pan for gold. Puts little nuggets and specks in his pan, covers them with dirt, and the kids all clap when he sluices the gold back out. Dad takes busloads of tourists from Melbourne and all over around the town and mines and tells them everything. One time when the high school was short of teachers, Dad went up and politely asked the headmaster if he'd like Dad to teach some geography. Mr Freeman politely told Dad, 'I'm sorry, Mr Bagnall, you're not qualified.' Dad's not qualified because when Dad was little and living in Pentland and Australia was riding on the back of a sheep, Dad was offered a scholarship in Ipswich, but Bagnalls didn't have a sheep and ya can't ride a sheep all the way to Ipswich anyway.

Dad goes *tinker-tinker-tink, tink, tink* with his spoon against his glass and does a burp. Dad drinks bicarb of soda. Dad's got insomnia. Dad's got the itch. Dad gets bad migraines and gets electric shocks. Dad's only got one kidney because he didn't drink enough water and Mum's gonna give him one if he needs it.

Reciprocal irritability: 'Dad, why's using 1080 on dingoes in the outback causing the crown-of-thorns to be eating up the Great Barrier Reef?'

'Answer her, Fred.'

Dad reads his paper.

Mum says, 'Go on, love.'

'Dingoes used to control the wild pigs by eating baby pigs. Now, wild pigs eat the turtle eggs in the estuaries; the turtles that used to swim out into the sea and eat … Oh, what's the point of tryin' to explain anything!'

Mum says, 'Fred! Your daughter's talking to you.'

Dad wets a finger on his tongue, turns a page.

When Dad's not looking, Mum signs at him with her thumb: *Up ya bum!*

'Come on, love,' Mum says. 'You're going to be late for school.'

'What's the point of going to school when they don't teach anything *useful?*'

When Mum's not looking, Dad looks above his paper, says, 'Pull ya skull in!'

I won. Sometimes winning feels like losing.

From my tree, I see high-school kids walking past. I wonder if I'd be any better off going to high school? They look tough, those girls. Scruffy. Streetwise. Savvy. Bet no one checks they're wearing white cottontail undies every morning on parade.

Someone's standing directly under the mango tree looking up. I hide my cigarette in my hand. Dumb! It's Greg. He's got some time to shoe my new mare, Natasha. 'Coming?'

Greg says nothing about catching me smoking up a mango tree, but, as we're going out to Greg's ute, he puts a hand on my shoulder. 'What's wrong, matey?'

'D'ya reckon you could teach me how to fight?'

*

Sunday night. I'm reading in bed.

'Sweetheart.' Mum pushes my book down. 'Talk to me.'

I raise my book, turn a page, pretend I'm reading. *Can't you see I'm reading!*

No point in talking to Mum about *Of Mice and Men*; Mum's never read it. Mum only reads *Women's Weekly* while she's catching forty winks at the back of the cafe in the afternoons. I do my talk in my head: *Good stories don't need action and suspense. Good stories explore the common experience. Good morning class, my review today...* George and Lennie are two displaced migrant ranch workers who go from ranch to ranch looking for work during the Great Depression in California. All George and Lennie want is to settle down on their own patch of dirt, and all Lennie wants is to look after and tend the rabbits. At the end, when George shoots Lennie in the back of the head, you *know* George has to do it; you *understand* George has got to kill Lennie, but you can't help wishing it had all somehow turned out different.

'Speak to me, sweetheart,' Mum says. 'Tell me what's wrong.'

Go away! Go away! Go away! Can't you see I'm reading!

Thirty-eight Hodgkinson Street is good for Mum. It's one street back from the main street, and it was only a block and a half to carry her cash box when she had to walk home late at night—until she bought Dad a Mini Moke to go to work, so we have two cars now.

Hodgkinson Street is handy, but there are no kids in Hodgkinson Street.

Next door is an old curtain twitcher called Mrs Young. Next door again is Herbert Hall, funeral directors, and across that street is the courthouse. Mrs Young called the police on Dad one night. Police came but police didn't see nothing wrong with peeing on your own pine trees in your own backyard late at night when you don't know anyone is watching. Dad would've had a lot more explaining to do if the police had knocked down the besser-block wall he built behind the barbie; that's where Dad hid the little hand pistol and bullets he had left over from the war and is not allowed to have anymore so he put it in the wall. *Why'd ya put it in the wall? Seemed like a good idea at the time.* On the other side of our house is the Salvation Army church. You only see someone there on a Sunday, and hear old ladies singing: 'Onward Christian Soldiers'. The minister keeps chooks up the back. Used to have three roosters too but the roosters kept waking Dad up, so one night the roosters disappeared. Some old blackfella Mum knows on the other side of town woke up next morning—*Praise the Lord!*—three roosters in his chook pen. Across the road is the Catholic Church hall where Greg and Robyn had their reception. Best wedding ever! Betty and I were bridesmaids, and Robyn was so beautiful I cried and had to wipe my nose on my glove because I didn't have a hanky, and Sheila Miller was matron of honour. Sheila's the prettiest girl in all Charters Towers, and you can't tell she's got a glass eye even if you look at it.

Betty and her boyfriend took me to my first dance. I'm never going to a dance again.

'What should I do if a boy I don't like asks me to dance?'

'It takes a lot of courage for a boy to walk across a hall to ask a girl to dance, so you shouldn't say no.'

Horticultural Hall is a big old hall in Mosman Street. Some say it should be condemned. Some say one day when 200 people start jumping up and down, the floor's gonna fall through. 'Not ever say no?' There are rickety steps and smelly dunnies down the back. 'Not unless he's been drinking; then you say, no, thank you very much.' I've got no intentions of going to the dunny. Spent all day with my hair in rollers. 'I'll pick you up at ten o'clock.' Got a new silk blouse and pink hotpants Mum ran up for me. 'It won't even get started by ten!' Got white lace-up boots up to my knees. 'Ten o'clock! You be waiting out the front.' Even got stockings on and some of Betty's bright blue shiny eye shadow. 'You been into my makeup?'

'Didn't use much!'

One thing I know is how to dance. Can't wait to show everyone how I can dance. I'm sitting on the platform seats wondering how wallflowers sit so I won't be sitting like one. I see Stanley Whorton across the hall. Stanley must be more than thirty now, but he still carries one arm up like a chicken and walks with one leg swinging out. I'm feeling ever so sorry for Stanley; he's asking one girl after another to dance, and they just giggle and run away.

No! No! No! Not me!

I'm admiring the walls—*Can't ya see I'm admiring the walls?*— but Stanley comes and asks me anyway. Stanley's not drunk, but he might as well be. I dance with Stanley and other girls stop dancing and cack themselves laughing. Spent the whole dance bracket dancing with Stanley, praying the floor would fall through. Nine thirty, the whole hall is whooping and hollering about how much Running Bear loves little White Dove; I'm standing out the front, looking up and down the street like I might have somewhere important to be.

'Did you have a good time, love?'

'You're late! You said ten o'clock!'

I hate Charters Towers. Charters Towers is full of spastics.

And I hate Mum too—making me dance with spastics.

'Well, if you're not going to talk to me, I might as well go to bed.'

Don't go! Don't go! Don't go!

Mum knows Jan left St Gabes. Mum doesn't know I've lost my best friend for good.

We're in the science lab, last lesson, Tuesday afternoon. It's hot.

Mudguts is writing on the board. All Mudguts wants is a bit of peace and quiet on a hot Tuesday afternoon, so we're supposed to be watching *Mating Habits of the Kangaroo.* I'm the only one watching, but when a big red buck hops aboard a little grey doe, I look down and doodle on my pad, and I'm glad no one is watching.

Us kids used to gawk at Granny's bulls doing that to cows, but that doesn't mean you want to watch it in a room full of boys.

Jan's gone down the back to talk with Bullseye. Gabes is so broke, Gabes will take anyone. New headmistress—been brought in to straighten out bad girls—carries her cane everywhere she goes. And uses it. Girls say she used to be a bikie's moll. Girls say she's a lesbian. Girls say all sorts of rot. Michelle Bullsy's bad news: been expelled, came to Gabes with a bad reputation and her own nickname. I don't have a nickname. (They tried *Beanpole, Brainbox* and *Bag of bones* but they didn't stick.) Bullseye and Jan have proper boobs and boyfriends. Jan's telling the truth; Bullseye might be lying. Anyway, Jan's showing Bullseye a photo of Doopy leaning on the bonnet of his V8 purple panel van. Bullseye's lieutenant and wannabes are rubbernecking and looking at Jan with new respect.

I see the back bench is empty; there's smoke climbing up behind it. Joey and Steven have been daring each other for weeks, but I didn't think they'd do it.

I flick ahead in *Web of Life.* I was going to be a vet till we started doing Science. Not just because a big red buck's trying to put a long pink thing inside the doe; it's more about the toads. I used to feel sorry for Mudguts having to put up with Grade Nine kids, until the toads. What I hated most about the toads was how Mudguts was all busy and important when he brought two buckets full of toads into the classroom. First time in the history of Grade Nine Science other kids paid attention. I hated Mudguts and I hated the kids all clustered around the benches while Mudguts caught a toad by the hind legs and the girls all squealed. I didn't mind toads, didn't think I'd mind cutting one up when it was dead ... *Thwack!* Mudguts whacked the toad's head on the bench, holding it by its hind legs, 'That stuns him.' Then with a needle: 'You push it into the brain like that, and wiggle it about.' There wasn't one damned kid in the class gave a rat's arse that *dissectors turned to frogs, which show changes in respiration and nervous conductivity, and have the convenience of foot webbing for viewing blood circulation in the periphery.* All the kids were watching what was adult-sanctioned killing, and showing off their own reactions to it. We all had a toad belly up on our benches with its little hands pinned back, but Mudguts didn't mash our toad's brain enough. When I started cutting, our toad tore his little hand from the pin and tried to push the scalpel away.

Mudguts has a dead cat in the fridge out back for senior kids to cut up—*larger, more multiplex organisms are required.* I wonder how many of the senior kids give a rat's arse that *mammals have to be strapped to the bench if the mysteries of mammalian physiology are to be elucidated.* And I'm sure as hell not interested in *testing the hypothesis that morphine dulls the perception of pain by injecting mice and observing their feet smouldering on a laboratory hotplate.* I shut my book.

Mudguts turns the video off, strokes his goatee. 'Now copy down these notes.'

Jan comes back to our bench, puts Doopy and his V8 purple panel van in her diary.

Girls down the back are giggling. I don't hear what they say, but Jan swivels on her stool. 'Come 'ere an' say it!'

Mudguts leans back against the board. His eyes dart back and forth above his glasses. Mudguts looks at his watch. Mudguts has never had a silent class before and he's praying for the bell. 'Now copy down these notes!' Sweat from Mudguts's back has blotched patches of the writing where he leaned against the board. On any other day, Grade Nine monkeys would be rattling their cages. 'Can't read it, sir! It's all smudged.'

Doesn't matter; no one's interested in Mudguts and his notes.

Bullseye's pretending she didn't hear, so Jan says louder, 'Come 'ere an' say it!'

Two heads bob up from the back bench; two cigarettes are flicked out the window.

Whole class is watching, so Bullseye has no choice. She strides up to our bench, juts her chin at Jan. 'You're a slut!' She says it loud and clear, but she's quick to turn away.

Not quick enough. Jan's hand catches Bullseye's jutting chin. Jan heel-punches Bullseye so hard, Bullseye flounders backwards, trying to catch up with her head. Bullseye catches a stool instead, crashes to the floor, legs and stool all tangled.

'You!' Mudguts shouts at Bullseye lying on the floor. 'Get to the principal's office.'

Bullseye flounces out, swipes Jan's books off the bench—ducks this time—and runs.

Mudguts has twenty-six pairs of eyes on him: *Your move, Mudguts*. Mudguts mops his brow, points at Jan, says more reasonably. 'You, pick those ...'

'Stick ya school up ya fat arse!' Jan kicks *Web of Life* so high Mudguts has to duck.

Deputy's standing at the door. Mr Burry doesn't say anything. Mr Burry doesn't have to say anything. Mr Burry's holding two half-smoked cigarettes between thumb and forefinger; he jabs them, once, twice, at the back bench, jerks a thumb towards his office.

Joey and Steven touch their chests: *Us?* Afternoon bell rings.

We're sitting on hay bales out the back of Alloway's shop.

'What're we gonna do?'

'What d'ya mean "we"?' Jan grins at me. 'I'm not comin' back.'

'But you have to! You're not fifteen.'

'Nah, I'm not comin' back. Yer can stick yer school up ya skinny arse.'

Next day, Bullseye's full of what she *woulda* done, *coulda* done, *shoulda* done to Jan.

All day, senior boys admire Joey's and Steven's cuts—not welts: cuts so deep down their legs they can still be made to bleed.

'If you won't talk to me, love,' Mum says. 'I can't help you.'

I say, 'Best laid schemes o' mice an' men, gang aft agley.'

Mum won't know what it means. Mum doesn't know anything.

I drop my book on the floor, turn out the bed light.

We all gotta play the hand we're dealt, but that doesn't stop you wishing you could restack the deck for a better outcome. The day after she walked out of Gabes, Jan enrolled herself in the local high school—walked out the day she turned fifteen, and won the Inaugural Charters Towers 50K Endurance Ride.

Mum knows Jan's left St Gabes. Mum doesn't know I've lost my best friend for good. Mum doesn't know that I am—by default—Bullseye's target.

Jan was … fearless.

Me? Not so much.

But just so many times a girl can get called *Pansy-won't-fight!*

*

Greg gets up at 4 am, rides racehorses track work, works at the butcher shop till 4.30 pm, then sometimes comes to our place to wait for Robyn—her photo's just been in the paper for being the first female ever made a bank teller in all of Queensland. On Sundays Greg runs the Crown Hotel for the Carolyns—*gonna take five years off our mortgage working Sundays*—and Betty's going to work full-time at the Crown too.

Heaven forbid! A daughter of Fred Bagnall's working as a barmaid!

'Money's twice as good as Bartlams, Dad.'

'Barmaids don't have bad reputations nowadays, Fred.'

On our front lawn, after he's done with work, Greg teaches me hip throw, shoulder throw, headlock, leg lock—that's the Indian Death Lock where you lock their legs and you can twist their little toe until they squeal.

I really don't want to do it, but kneeling in chapel, someone's behind me whisperin' *Pansy! Pansy! Pansy-won't-fight!* Line up for class and someone's giggling *Pansy! Pansy! Pansy-won't-fight!* Queue in the dining room … Notes left on the desk …

If you were little you could say, *Sticks and stones will break my bones, but names will never hurt me!* Everyone knows you just have to be grown up and ignore it, but when kids in other grades start saying *Pansy-won't-fight*, I have to pick my day: Wednesday after lunch.

Bullseye's lieutenant is from New Guinea. She has a scar on her head where a Kanaka climbed through her bedroom window one night and hit her with an axe. I got my scar on my head from a kid's yellow swing. Wednesdays, Bullseye's lieutenant does Phys Ed down on the sports field; Bullseye does Home Ec here, in the girls common room. No lieutenant Wednesday afternoon, and only wannabes to help Bullseye mash me. And no boys to see me getting mashed by Bullseye—only Fairy does Home Ec, and he doesn't count.

I still don't know if I'm gonna do it. *If she doesn't say it, I won't do it.*

I'm standing at the door. Bullseye breezes up. 'How's the weather up there, Pansy?'

She didn't really say *it*, but I'm so wound up. 'Come on, then!' I step in front of her. 'Outside on the lawn.'

All the way down three stairs my kneecaps are jumping up and down. I'm thinking she's behind me and I'm thinking how disappointed all the teachers are gonna be. I can even hear Mr Burry saying: *Good girls don't fight.* I'm on the lawn, can't breathe. *Gotta get her in a headlock; if I can just get her in a headlock ...*

I turn around; she's not there. I go weak. Bullseye's gone into the classroom.

Home Ec teacher comes out. 'What are you waiting for Pam? Bell's gone.'

I say real loud, 'Waiting for Bullseye, Mrs Boyd.'

She doesn't come.

No one calls me Pansy anymore, but somehow I don't feel good about it.

I cut off all my hair. Cut it myself. Now when I sit up in the mango tree I look like David Bowie, smoking B&H, because only girls smoke Alpine.

Mum and Dad have their tickets booked to America for a holiday. Betty's going too, but I said I didn't want to go; I didn't want to miss riding in the Charters Towers Show on my new mare, Natasha. But they should have made me go. I'm just a stupid kid, so what would I know?

My best film of all time is *Soldier Blue*. In 1970, Dotson Rader of *The New York Times* wrote *Soldier Blue* 'must be numbered among the most significant, the most brutal and liberating, the most honest American films ever made'. Why am I telling you this? Because time was, the world was black and white: good guys wore white hats, bad guys wore black, and Jan and I were blood brothers, gonna be best friends forever.

Time was, Indians were low-life-thievin' redskins, sneakin' around lookin' to scalp innocent white fellas; then along comes *Soldier Blue* telling how it was white fellas did the scalping first, white fellas cut off breasts and testicles for tobacco pouches. *Soldier Blue* shows the brutality of 700 army men as they wipe out 500 Indians, most of them women and children—a massacre so vicious it became known as the most shameful day in the Indian Wars of the American West.

So I'm just wondering: if Americans aren't the good guys, who the damned hell is?

Like, I felt good the afternoon Bullseye ran inside—*I am woman!*—but then I got to thinking: when Jan put Bullseye on her bum, Mudguts yelled at Bullseye still lying on the floor; Mudguts didn't yell at Jan. Bullseye didn't run away from me *per se*. Bullseye was smart enough to know I had the lesbian bikie's moll and her cane in my corner.

And I'd known too.

If Exclusion^2 + Individual = x; what's x worth?

Can't do *that* in my head. Seems like the more I learn, the less I know. I mean, if the world got tipped upside down, do you think we'd notice? Gravity says *down* would still be in the same direction.

Only constant in a world gone grey is Granny Chapman.

Wish I'd known Elizabeth May Chapman, and not just mean old Granny.

*

14 March 1974

May Chapman waved, but brought her hand down quickly.

She watched the Moke become a speck: no rolling dust clouds signing off departures these days; no red dust heralding arrivals either: one lane of bitumen all the way to town, more's the pity. Still, it was good of Bet to come, knowing she was on her own. Game of scrabble with Betty had passed the afternoon.

It was good of Robyn and Greg to come last weekend. *Shouldn't've come out, silly buggers—not with Robyn due any day now.* 'If it's a girl, we're going to name her after you, Grandma: Deborah May.'

May rubbed her arm. *Silly bugger! Only went and pulled a muscle last night tryin' to start the generator. Not much good havin' the electric when yer can't start the generator.* Doesn't matter, she'd get an early night. *Like to be upstairs before it's proper dark. Got a big day tomorra.*

But she wouldn't go in just yet; too early to go in yet.

Across the road, she could see her new bulls milling at the trough. *All wrong, those bulls: all big grey humps an' big floppy ears; high-strung too, not like her good old Herefords. Weigh in at 2000 pounds those bulls—1000 kilos.*

Metric! Just something else she had to get used to.

'Yer just might run yer eye over them new bulls, Greg, tell me what yer reckon. Didn't wanna be gettin' into Brahmans ... Ian said we oughta.'

Too many changes these days: Zebu bred in India! When folks been breeding Herefords hundred years or more. 'What do you reckon, Greg?'

'Handle the heat better than European breeds, Grandma. Got more sweat glands, oily skin—tick resistant—won't have to be mustering and dipping all the time.'

She would have liked to ask Dick what he thought about Brahmans. Never heard of Brahmans till after Dick died.

All events predicated: before Dick died; after Dick died …

Ah, well, time'll tell.

Browning blossom at her feet. Christmas trees have run their season's riot.

She reached for a purple blossom, but pulled her arm down quickly. *More'n just a muscle; must've pinched a nerve.* She flicked her wrist, tamped the palm. *Damned arm!*

Summer was done, and the air was hazy with the promise of a long hot autumn. Long shadows leaned across the lawn—proof the world still turned. *Time to go in.*

Dinner? *Got a bit of cold corned meat; got a bit of leftovers. Doctor's always after her about diet these days. Get upstairs before it's proper dark.* Seems like everyone's after her these days. Now she was by herself on weekends. *You've gotta get the phone on, Mum!*

Never yusta take a breath, not halfway up the stairs.

Never yusta lock doors. Times change.

Next thing you know, they'd be telling her she had to move to town. Worse, pack her off to Eventide. Drop dead before she'd live in Eventide. Could never live in town.

But bloody bitumen had gone and brought town out to her. *Young louts! Come out in their cars … cut fences … go round shootin' up the place, leavin' stubbies.*

Rifle beside the bed. *Never had to use it. Times change.*

Too much change: world she knew and loved was dying.

Girls hav'ta live their own lives. Dulce lives in town, four boys goin' to school. June gone to Townsville, an' Melva at her shop … She worried about her girls.

Not Ollie. Fred'll look after Ollie.

Might just lie down for a bit … no good. *Know what caused that back pain, don't ya? Went and fell down an old post hole yesterdy!* Went down up to the knee—had the devil of a job hoisting herself back out. *But hav'ta be up the yards when they bring in cattle. Like to keep an eye on things.* No good. *Try Dick's pillow. Can breathe a bit better sittin' propped up like that. That's better ...*

No good. Might get a bit of sleep sittin' in Ollie's rocker. Didn't like that rocker Ollie gave her for Christmas. *What'd she be wantin' with a rocker? Comfy, though.*

One foot on the floor: little rock, like that ...

Might havta go inta town tomorra ...

Prob'ly shouldn't wait till Friday ...

Maybe get the phone on ...

Moonlight on bevelled glass sprinkled colour on the wall: patterns red and violet. *You left me: there one day, not the next. No goodbyes. No regrets.*

May knew the clamouring world and her place in it too well to harbour illusions: she was an old woman now but sometimes, just sometimes, she was still the little goat girl from Begorra Waterhole. As a child turns a kaleidoscope, she could see patterns slide, elide: *photo of Dick, Ollie saved ...* Wished she could've shared the day the river became a sea ... with Dick.

God? Too busy livin' to be worried about dyin'.

A fleeting thought, spiritual and intuitive: *in the end, it all comes down to dying.* Her sober spirit carried her from one keepsake to another: wedding photo ... utterances of love ... and hatred, too incoherent for words ... She could feel his presence—a hollow presence, coloured by imaginings: flesh can never live up to memory and absence. Thirty years, hers had been a monologue: the sound of one hand clapping...

Such thoughts were not consoling.

But if the purpose of life is to matter, to count, to stand for something, to have it make a difference that we ever lived at all?

Counselled by her soul, in her mind's eye a little goat girl from Begorra Waterhole could see pools of light on redwood ... could smell Christmas dinners long since digested ... could hear

141

the ghostly murmur of table talk, conversations long forgotten ...
receding noise of worldly voices.

All her joys, sorrows, tragedies behind her now.

'Just one more Christmas, God,' Elizabeth May Chapman
murmured. 'Just one more.'

In Loving Memory of our mother
Elizabeth May Chapman
Died 14th March, 1974
Aged 74
At Rest

*

Northern Miner: April 1974

'AT REST', BY FF BAGNALL

For the past 30 years I have spent every Christmas at Fletcherview.
Because of this, I feel compelled to write these few lines as a token
of appreciation, not only from myself and the Bagnall family,
but also from my three brothers-in-law and their families, to one
who has always been a source of great help and inspiration to
each and every one of us.

When Elizabeth May Chapman passed away recently, so
ended an era, an era dating back to 1945 when her husband
was killed, leaving four teenage daughters, all of whom have
since married and reared families in the district. We've had our
differences—who hasn't—but all these have been forgotten on
Christmas Day each year when her descendants have gathered at
Fletcherview in a spirit of togetherness and good will.

At first, there were only a few but as the years passed more
grandchildren arrived and finally filled the table built for twenty.

Christmas dinner was not only provided, but always cooked by 'Grandma'. Every year during school holidays, she was host to an ever-increasing number of grandchildren, and it is these in particular who would like to say a heartfelt farewell to 'Granny Chapman of Fletcherview'.

We mourn her loss—and the loss of another link to the early days of Charters Towers.

*

Fletcherview: November 1975

'You be careful on that damned horse! Pammie ...'

'Don't bug me, Mum! I won't be long.'

Landscape so vast, even the sound of hoof beats surrenders to the silence.

I halt Big Blue on the banks of the anabranch.

Seduced by the mystery of the place, time and space conspire with ghostly whispers: *Come on then, Peggy. Let's you and me go and get some pepper ...*

Stand in the stirrups; run a hand over smooth white bark: names, carved and grown beyond my reach. Stare up into the sun-spangled leaves—*Youse kids come down outta there! Before yers break yer flamin' necks!* The sounds of children playing out small dramas, where bigger dramas have unfolded.

I am seventeen; got a little Kodak pocket Instamatic—and a mission: not just any old photo: *this particular photo*, taken from *this particular position ...*

I canter Blue down towards Big Sandy. On the banks, fresh clumps of debris in high branches speak of last year's flood; on the lower banks, wild pigs wallow in tepid pools of scum. The summer rains have yet to come, but storm clouds have been building.

143

Above me, the sky is kiln-burnt blue; up ahead the old house stands against a backdrop, black and heavy. I'm going to lose light soon.

Dismount at the garden gate, *where my mother met my father*.

Front lawns are dead, chook yard empty. In the dining room, the only sound is the hollow footfall of my riding boots on concrete. *You're not supposed to be here ...* I pass through the kitchen. Out the back, up there near the turkey shed, is my objective: that tank stand—must be more than forty foot high, that stand. From up there, I'll be able to look down, show the main roof line, the casement windows, and the steep, steep slant of the kitchen roof.

Without someone to keep the ghosts alive, the old homestead might just as well be dead.

9

The beginning of the end

Charters Towers: June 2010

I've started having this dream: backstage is busyness—dim lights, whispered words, running feet; rehearsals for reversals muttering, stuttering, words that grasp at meaning. Tweak the curtain: shadows move down aisles, climb knees, murmuring apologies.

No script. No rehearsal. Curtains going up and ... God, I don't know my lines!

Betty: Police brought Mum home today, found her walking down near the Waverley.

Me: My flight gets in at two thirty. Can you pick me up?

Betty's going grey. Betty has a bit of lunch on her blouse. Betty has a knot of silver masking tape sitting on her nose. *Glasses broke!* Betty's wearing one sandal, carrying the other one. *Sandal broke!* Betty has a station wagon full of car parts. *Gotta get this bumper to Bill before he knocks off work.* Betty drives with one foot on the passenger dashboard, one hand in a packet of Allen's snakes.

Betty: Thought you were gonna cut down on sugar?

Me: Thought you were gonna cut down on smokes.

I owe the best year of my life to Betty: she did Europe on five dollars a day, and I tagged along. Betty carried a two-man tent on her backpack because I'm just the baby, put the tent up every night because I'm just the baby. Betty posed beneath the signpost 'Bagnall' in Staffordshire in England, and sat on a footpath mosaic 'Chapman' outside a chemist shop in Ireland.

What I remember most about our ancestors is playing with a big black dog on an Irish beach and doing cartwheels in the rain. Betty remembers chasing that big black dog down the beach—and the chunk of Edam in its mouth.

Only black dog in those days frolicked in the rain, stole your cheese and ran away.

It's good to be home. Home is King Street, Charters Towers, but *home* is where the mother is.

Black dog sniffed around King Street when Dad handed in his licence: *ninety-year-old, got no business driving.* Dad has a gopher now, a little electric scooter; only Mum's car in the garage now. Betty's panel-beater husband, Bill, did a good job on it—no evidence of the smash.

Mum and Dad are waiting at the gate.

Little dog rushes out says, *Hello! Hello! Wanna go for a walk?*

'Not now, Misty.'

Happy birthday to you; you've reached ninety-two. 'Happy birthday, Dad.'

Dad sticks a big hand out. 'What's happy about it?' I shake his big hand, put my arms around his shoulders. He leans forward; 1.2 seconds later, he pats my arm. *Time's up.*

No time limit on Mum. Mum tucks her head under my chin and really holds me.

Dad puts the kettle on. Mum follows me and my suitcase down the hall.

I really hold her. She really holds me.

'So, what were you thinking, walking down to the Waverley, silly chook?'

'Don't know what I was thinking, love—silly as a wheel.'

Tea's on. *Might clean up around Grandma's grave while you're home.*

Might take a run out to Fletcherview, boil the billy, while you're home.

Might go out and visit the anabranch ...

'You have a game of chess with your father. Dad's been looking for a game. Haven't you, Fred? Fred, have a game with Pam. We can start on the house tomorrow.'

We go onto the big deck out the back. Wood needs oil; nearly a year since I did it.

'Gotta do me garden.' Only two steps down, Mum runs down, to show off that she can. Dad stands on the step, coos. A white dove flutters down from the chook shed, sits on his wrist and pecks at the seed in his hand. 'Must've escaped from somewhere, comes every afternoon.'

Mum's so tiny ...

Dad's snared my queen. Mum runs up the stairs, to show me that she can.

Checkmate—five moves. Usually takes him longer.

I'm listening to thumps coming from Mum's bedroom. The drawer in her dresser has come off the runners; Mum's thumping it with a hip, trying to force it shut.

'I've looked everywhere, it's gone!'

'No, Mum, I'm sure the cleaning lady didn't take it. It'll turn up.'

'Silly bugger!' Mum starts crying. 'Wish they'd just take me out and shoot me!'

'Mum, it doesn't matter. It's just a silly watch. We'll go downtown tomorrow, buy another one—'

'It's not a silly watch!' Mum wails. 'Robyn gave me that watch.'
Oh, Mum …

'Fred! You're not taking that dog! You take Misty, Pam. Tripped Dad up last time. Came home, hands and knees all cut. Take Dad's stick—big dogs come running out.'

Misty's kennel used to be a clothes dryer. I bought it when Mum had her hysterectomy and was having trouble hanging clothes on the line. Dryer gave up the ghost years ago—*If we turn it this way, Dad, Misty can hop in through the round hole, see?*

King Street: dead-end street, parkland in front, vacant block behind, big backyard. Dad corners me at his vegie patch. 'Ground's not so good here: only got these beans in. Birds got the paw-paws.' Dad turns to me and says: 'I should have been told. Why didn't you tell me?'

'I know, Dad. In retrospect, I would've told you sooner, but …'

Don't tell Mum and Dad. I don't want them upset … I'm going to outlive them … Ruth Cilento's diet … Greg's planted a vegie patch …

'Come on, Misty.' It's a beautiful evening. Weather's perfect.

Charters Towers isn't the dry dust bowl I remember as a kid; the highway's lined with big African mahoganies and garden beds. Eventide backs onto King Street, where Mum and Dad have lived for a decade. Eventide fronts the Lynd Highway, which heads out to the anabranch, where Mum and Dad lived for two decades after Grandma died. Built a home on the same spot Dad trapped possums in '36, adopted Peggy the pig in '44—and met Mum.

Only moved to town when living out bush became too much for them.

Little green Moke on a one-lane, unmarked strip of bitumen with a fully loaded, double-decker, two-dog semitrailer up your bum.

'Get off the road, Dad! You've got a semi up your bum!'

'I'm sitting right on the speed limit.' A finger taps the speedo. 'Look!'

'Keep your eyes on the road! And get off it! He can't slow down!'

'Why not?' Eyes stare ahead; knuckles whiten on the wheel. 'He's got brakes.'

'Not anymore, he doesn't! Get … off … the … road, Dad!'

The park opposite Eventide has a statue of a man and horse, and another man panning for gold in a man-made creek. Next street over is St Gabes. School finally went guts-up years ago. Main administration is a B & B. Girls all board over at All Souls now—All Souls St Gabriels. And there's the little chapel where Mum and Dad were married. Mum and Dad coming down those steps: black and white, sunlight on confetti …

I go along Deighton Street. Robyn and Greg's first home. Knocked their mortgage over in nine years. But only *really rolled 'er* when Greg started Dalrymple Pastoral Agency in partnership with Milt Evans.

That was before they moved to Townsville so their girls could go to Grammar.

Home again. Mum's rummaging in Dad's garden shed.

'What's she doing?'

'What are you doing out here, Mum?'

'Gotta feed my chookies, love.'

'That's Omo, Mum. Here's your chook feed … sweetheart, let me do it.'

'Silly bugger! Silly as a wheel. Thank you, love. There you go, chookies.'

'Come on, Mum, we'll—'

'Just gotta feed my chookies, love …'

'We'll start on the house tomorrow.'

'I can drive! Don't you think I can drive? Still a good driver! Aren't I, Fred?'

'Of course you are, Mum. Just thought you'd like me to. Here you go, you can ...'

'No, you drive, love. Better if you drive.'

I take the scenic route. Dad points out who lives where, since when, and who used to live over there before he/she died. Mum says, 'And there's the stop sign, love. I stopped there, but that man must've been going way too fast, to hit me. Even the policeman said that man must've been going way too fast.'

Stink! Lissner Park is being wrecked by bats. Dad's one-man crusade: 'Used to shoot them. Before I die, I've got a good mind to ...'

A lot of country towns are dying. Charters Towers isn't. The main street is bumper-to-bumper traffic. There's Mum's cafe—Alford Arcade now: print shop and hairdresser. The Regent Theatre across the road is a Treasure Kingdom; Robyn and Greg's Country Kitchen is a Telstra shop. At the top end of the street, opposite the post office, Poppet Head is still Poppet Head. Robyn started that gift shop; Greg ran the Suncorp Agency from it.

No silvertails in our family. Robyn didn't need a silver spoon; Robyn had a four-leaf clover ... before they moved to Brisbane so their girls could go to uni. Before Betty phoned.

'I'll bring Mum and Dad up to your place for the weekend.'

'Me? You want me to tell them, Betty? But I'm just the baby ...'

Innisfail—the sort of house that when you were a kid you'd drive past and look up in wonder: *How can anyone be so lucky, to live in a house like that?* House on a hill and fourteen acres; green slopes, banana fields and paw-paws; pine forests and early morning mists. Crocs sunbathe on the banks of the Johnstone River. *See that one down there, Mum? Look, Dad, one on the far bank too.* Cyclone Larry is still two years away so the rainforest backdrop of my house is white cedars, palms, brilliant orange African tulips and a riot of wait-a-while vine.

'Betty, you show Mum those bromeliads … and those orchids.

'Come up the back, look at my tank, Dad.'

From the crest behind my house, Dad admires the sunset, says, 'Mount Bartle Frere: highest mountain in Queensland, 5322 feet. Named after Sir Henry Bartle Frere, British Governor of Cape Colony at the outset of the Zulu Wars.'

He's not as tall as me anymore—I realise too, if our whole attention is focused on that which is not there, we fail to see what is there. Dad's an interesting man because he's interested. He's eighty-seven and still has a thirst for knowledge and a desire to know and understand the physical world.

'This house is wasted on you.'

'Thanks a lot, Dad.'

'No, I just mean beautiful big home like this needs a family.'

'Thanks a lot, Dad.'

'I didn't mean—'

'Dad.' I interrupt him. 'Heard the expression: Don't shoot the messenger?'

He leans on his walking stick, leans in closer because he's going deaf. Serious blue-grey eyes look at me intently above his glasses.

He lets me put an arm around his shoulders as we go back inside.

And the world turns on.

It was never going to be this way. I always imagined they would come and live with me. *Old folk, sipping cups of tea, reminiscing by the fire, blanket on their knees.* It was never meant to be this way:

'What about all these books, Dad? And thirty years of *National Geographic.*'

'That box is going to the library, that one to the Over Fifty's Club; and that one …'

I put Dad's three books on top of the third box: *North Queensland Cavalcade: A history of Charters Towers and other stories* (1979);

Golden Heritage: A brief history of Charters Towers and some of its people (1983) and his third book, *People*, which nearly brought him unstuck. He set out to do a brief biography of anyone who was anyone in the town. Called for expressions of interest, and had half the town knocking on his door. Pity half the town had been divorced, been remarried, had illegitimate kids and lived in sin.

I lived in sin. With a Pom. *Dr* Pom to you: PhD in English Lit. He tried to teach me where, to put commas, but, I never really got it; tried to tell me Hamlet's *not just a poofter wearing tights!* and imported the first red-nosed pitbulls into Australia.

Relationship tombstone reads: Death by Neglect, and inability to master commas.

A shrink would probably tell you: from my dad to my own 'daddy', I passed the power of judgement I confused with love.

I'd tell you: English entitlement met colonial cringe.

And here's a framed photo of Robyn swimming with dolphins. Before Greg phoned.

'Matey ...' Indrawn breath, shaky exhale.

Silence.

'Matey ...'

Twenty minutes I held the phone. Greg couldn't say the words.

That's all right; I didn't want to hear them.

A minute is neither more nor less than the sum of its seconds, but the world was about to change. Forever.

'Matey, it's time to come ...'

Dad catches me looking at the photo of Robyn swimming with dolphins, and repeats, 'I should have been told. Why didn't you tell me?'

'I know, Dad. I'm sorry. In retrospect I would've told you sooner, but ...'

Don't tell Mum and Dad. I'm going to outlive them ...

On top of Dad's three books I put Mr Buchanan awarding Dad Citizen of the Year, 2008, at the Australia Day Awards. Three nominations—one from the *Northern Miner*. And Robyn swimming with dolphins.

'I should have been told.'

'I know, Dad. I'm truly sorry, but Mum was really unwell at the time ...'

His big hand makes a definitive gesture: *I should have been told! I know ... and ... I'm sorry.*

Betty comes every day and inspects the wheelie bin. 'You can't throw that out! I'll take it out to my place.'

Mum: Man up the road wants my chookies.

Dad: Lady who bought the house will take Misty.

Betty: Black Pete's going to take the car.

'What about this clown, Mum? Surely it can go out?'

'Oh, no, love. I can't throw out Cokie.'

Cokie is a bed-sitting clown with dirty big red boots. I sit Cokie on the 'maybe' pile. Cokie has red hair, pale skin, red nose, patched tweed clothes and a mouldy four-leaf clover sprouting from his hat. The white ruff around Cokie's neck is grey, and the back half of Cokie's ceramic head is missing; it's a jagged hole. Four days Cokie watches me: pale painted face, big innocent eyes, huge freakish grin. Cokie finds it amusing: cobwebs on the lights; grime around the sink; dead flies on the windowsills and dead food in the fridge.

'Glad to be outta here. Just too much for me, can't manage anymore.'

'Come here, Mum. Don't be upset.'

'Just too much ...'

'Of course it's too much, Mum. Don't cry.'

Day before I'm due to leave Mum says, 'Go on, love, Cokie can go.'

'Are you sure, Mum?'

'Yes, love.'

I shove Cokie broken-head-first in the wheelie bin: *Take that you little fucker!*

*

Coolum: Mother's Day 2004 (6 years earlier)

Cairns Airport. I'm on a plane heading down to Brisbane. I don't want to be on a plane heading down to Brisbane. Robyn and Greg should never have left Charters Towers. Really inconvenient, having to be on a plane heading down to Brisbane.

'Welcome aboard ...'

I'm calm.

'Estimated flying time ...'

I feel nothing: I don't want to be on a plane to Brisbane.

Mum and Dad and Betty are on a plane from Townsville.

Mum and Dad and Betty don't want to be on a plane from Townsville heading down to Brisbane. You don't get on a plane to visit someone who has a cold; you don't get on a plane to visit someone who's going to get well ...

But here I am: on a plane ... going down to Brisbane, to go to Coolum ... to say goodbye to my big sister ... for forever.

Absurd word: forever.

Tears start. Won't stop.

Man beside me is uncomfortable.

I keep my face to the window.

Tears make no sound. Tears are silent.

'Welcome to Brisbane, please remain seated ...'

Man needs to say something. Poor dumb bastard says, 'Did you have a good flight?'

Poor dumb bitch says, 'Yes, thank you.'

So, here we are, in a car heading down to Coolum: so much traffic on the road; where are all these people going in such a hurry? Seems like every waking moment, the clock calls the shots: on bedside tables, in airport lounges, on wrists … tick-tick-ticking … rushing to meet the most important deadline of all.

Betty pulls into a servo. Betty's *gotta go to the loo*.

Mum pats my knee. 'Don't you wanna go, love?'

'No, I don't believe in it.' Personal rebellion against the laws of nature—and, by extension, God. The powerlessness of God without *us* is an intriguing thought—*We don't wanna play your stupid game no more, God!*—but only Dad gets it.

'I don't believe in it!' Dad repeats. 'I don't believe in it!' Dad laughs so hard he's crying.

It's confronting, when you realise that even God makes mistakes.

Robyn's two girls are home to celebrate Mother's Day. Champagne breakfast: *eat, drink and be merry for tomorrow I die.*

Robyn wants to know if her haircut is a good one. 'Is my hair nice?' she asks, running her fingers back through the fringe.

'Your hair's beautiful, Robyn.'

'Good,' Robyn says. 'I want to be a pretty corpse.'

Robyn doesn't have the cachectic look of the cancer patient; she doesn't have that look of someone close to the end—eighteen months on Ruth Cilento's diet has done that much for her. Robyn's hair is lustrously alive, and so is Robyn: 'Just waiting on my angel wings.'

Robyn didn't opt for the societal norm—part of that package included the advice that chemo would more than likely fail. *Leiomyosarcomas are malignant tumours of smooth muscle. Like leiomyomas, they can grow almost anywhere in the body. They tend to occur in adults, particularly the elderly.*

Robyn's fifty-four. Robyn has a husband who would die for her—with her, if not for their two daughters: Deborah May and Mia Elizabeth, named after Granny Chapman.

Deborah May sat on that same mosaic 'Chapman' footpath outside a chemist shop in Ireland, and brought home an Irish engineer. Their son, Finn O'Connell, is crawling on the bed. Baby Finn doesn't know he's here to say goodbye to his grandma.

We know. It's why we came.

Meabh Robyn, Olive May and Tadhg Gregory (not yet conceived) will never know what a wonderful woman their grandmother was.

We know. It's why we came.

In her prettiest nightie, Robyn sits up, takes tubes from her nose—*I want to look pretty*—two schoolfriends beside her raise their champagne glasses to the camera.

Greg changes the oxygen cylinder. *Don't leave me here alive, alone.*

Mia Elizabeth helps with a morphine injection. *Don't leave us, Mum.*

Deborah May takes baby Finn outside and cries.

Pulse of shoes on pavement … ocean breathes and sighs … moonlight etching white bones in the sea … a family, walking to a holiday unit at Coolum Beach, no white pebbles to show the way, just crumbs in this story.

'I should've been told.' Dad walks on. 'I should've been told!'

Sadness and grief are universal, but how we show these emotions—or hold them back for private moments—is learned. How very much better it would be to be ululating shadows dancing in the dark, howling at the moon: keening sounds in firelight.

Ancestral cry … Eye gouge … Teeth gnash … Beat and beat, rip and rent and tear.

I lie in bed, one heartbeat, one breath, one second at a time.

From the twin bed beside me—in the silence of the night—the sound of Betty sobbing.

She who was living is dead. And we, who are living, are not.

10

Home is where the mother is

Tenterfield: July 2010

I'm shivering on the veranda of a historic old Queenslander in New South Wales.

If you were to ask *why* I'm shivering on the veranda of a historic old Queenslander in New South Wales, I'd take off a glove, light a cigarette, narrow my eyes thoughtfully and tell you: 'Damned if I know!'

Coppabella: hobby farm, 120 acres of blue granite country outside Tenterfield. No one can see me sitting here on 120 acres, so I can blow smoke till the cows come home. Cows are coming home now. See them? They're coming up along the track from Brassington Creek—forty little Black Angus steers, headbutting an icy wind and kicking up their heels.

As anyone'll tell you, Black Angus are the flavour of the month in New South Wales.

Sun's just about to drop behind that hill; when it does, temperature will drop with it: five degrees now will bottom out at minus ten tonight. Wind's starting to kick up too.

Frig!

I still swear with my mates. My two best mates drink. My two best mates smoke. My two best mates fight—not just hair-pulling, eye-scratching, girlie kinds of fights: proper eye-gouging, knockdown, sink-the-boot, no-holds-barred kinds of fights.

So *why* am I sitting on the veranda of a Queenslander in New South Wales with red-belly blacks in the woodheap and quolls chewing off chooks' heads at night?

Just told ya: *Damned if I know!* Seemed like an idea at the time—but seems everywhere I go, I take my Self and Me. Me and my two mates spend a lot of time dissecting and inspecting our collective bellybutton on this veranda. Like the last time I went home.

'You'll love it, Mum.'

'Oooh, too cold for swimmin', love.'

'They've got a new indoor heated pool, Mum. Seatbelt on. There you go.'

'Is this your car, love?'

'No, it's Betty's car, Mum. Remember, I flew up?'

'Of course you did! Silly bugger!'

And there's the stop sign, love. I stopped there, but that man must've been going way too fast, to hit me. Even the policeman said he must've been going way too fast.

Mum's in her pretty blue swimsuit patterned with darker flowers; a little skirt, cut on the diagonal, runs from hip to thigh. It's a suit made for a young old lady and it suits my mum beautifully. 'Water's lovely, isn't it, Mum?'

'I'm all right, love.' Mum paddles her hands. 'You go on, love.'

Thought it was a good idea. *What did you think? That your mother was going to swim laps?* I thought she'd do some widths. Truly, I did. *Really?*

Mid-length I turn, swim back. Mum's hanging on to the step ladder. *She's frightened, you stupid bitch!* When she sees me, Mum

159

lets go of the ladder. Hands paddling the surface, she makes her way to me. Wet, the bathers float out around her; a strap comes off her shoulder as she paddles into my arms.

'That'll do me for today, Mum.'

'Don't be silly, love. I'm just being silly. Used to be a good swimmer. Just being silly, love. You keep going.'

'Betty's going to take us for a run out to the anabranch—boil the billy—so we might go and get ready. What do you think?'

'That'll be lovely, love.'

My arm on her waist, we wade over to the side. I steady her as she climbs.

'Wait there, Mum.' I climb up behind her. 'Wait for me, Mum!' I take her hand. 'You're such a good girl.' *And you're a silly bitch.*

We shower. I pat her dry, comb her hair, pack my flippers and goggles. 'Here, Mum, you've left your bathers.' I wring them out. 'Here you go.'

'You keep them, love.' Her hand pushes her bathers towards my backpack.

'Don't be silly, Mum, you look really pretty in them.'

'No, you keep them, love. I'm not going to need them anymore.'

Oh, Mum ...

'Hop in this door, Mum. Seatbelt. There you go.'

'Is this your car, love?'

'No, it's Betty's car, Mum.'

And there's the stop sign, love. I stopped there, but that man must've been going way too fast, to hit me. Even the policeman said he must've been going way too fast.

And what about the time Mum and Dad came to visit me in Tenterfield?

Betty put them on the plane and Mia Elizabeth and her Pommy husband—*Love Australia!*—picked them up in Brisbane. 'Oh dear, Granny, you've had a little accident. Never mind, there's a chemist just around the corner.' It was the first time Mum had had a little accident; now, every day. 'We're going out all day, Mum, so best wear these little panties.'

'Did you have a good trip, Dad?'

'Worst trip in all our lives.'

'Why?'

'Imagine waking in the middle of the night on the fourteenth floor and she's gone. Found her down the corridor, knocking at a door ... Sorry, sir, I've got her now.'

'I need to go to the toilet, Fred. Where's the toilet?'

It was a family reunion of sorts but, as Greg said, *our family's pretty skinny*—Deborah May and her Irishman lived in Ireland—and was about to get skinnier: Mia's Pommy husband had more recently been heard to say, 'Hate Australia!'

I have a photo of Dad climbing to the highest point of the ridge at Coppabella, pointing out mountains and rivers; a photo of Dad sitting on the quad bike—*Thumbs up!* A photo of Mum and Dad down at the Wallangarra Railway Station—just forty kay away—where they went on the first day of their honeymoon sixty-two years ago. Got a memory of Mum sidling up to me: 'Pammie!' Mum whispered. 'There's a strange man in your kitchen.'

'Come on, sweetheart, we'll have a look. That's Greg, Mum. You remember Greg?'

'Course I do, silly bugger.'

I have Granddad Dick in his brown fedora on the wall, green eyes looking down. On the bookcase Mum and Dad, sunlight on confetti, and Robyn, swimming with dolphins.

'I'm supposed to be her mother ... they didn't even let me say goodbye.'

I feel my mother's pain: a physical ache, deeper, heavier than my own.

We did, Mum. We all said goodbye to Robyn.

161

So here I am in Tenterfield, stone motherless cold.

Thud of boots on veranda! Hide my smoke in hand. *Dumb!*

He's got his gruff voice on. 'Thought you were gonna cut smokin', matey?'

Thought you were gonna come the other way, not come sneaking up behind me!

'Mum's birthday Saturday. I'm going up for a couple of weeks. Give Dad a break.'

'God it's cold!' Greg stamps his boots. 'Who'd wanna live here?'

'Frigged if I know!' Pull on a glove. 'Come inside, I'll light the fire.'

*

Charters Towers: July 2010

WELCOME TO EVENTIDE: HOSTEL—LOW CARE SECTION: At Eventide we aim to continue family life as much as possible and encourage your relatives and friends to be part of our family too, welcoming them to participate in all our fun activities.

Eventide Manual

Admin: They can't have a double bed. A double bed is against regulation!

Betty: They're havin' their double bed.

Admin: No double beds!

Betty: Bring it this way, boys.

Admin: It's against regulation! Fire hazard! Won't fit!

Betty: Told ya it'd fit.

Admin: Against regulation to wash double linen—

Betty: They're havin' their double bed.

Admin: For nurses to bend that low—

Betty: Double bed. (Piss off, fatso! *And so say all of us! And so say all …*)

Cokie smirks at me. Cokie's sitting on a veranda chair outside.

'Why on earth would you get that filthy clown out of the bin, Betty?'

'Why not? He's not hurting anyone. And Mum got him from Robyn's shop.'

They're waiting outside. Dad lets me hold him for 2.3 seconds, says against my ear, 'So glad you could come.'

No time limit on Mum. 'You shouldn't have come, love. Comin' all this way!'

'It's your birthday, Mum, of course I came.' *Happy birthday to you, you've reached eighty-two!*

Big shady mango trees—welcome in summer—make it dark inside: two adjoining rooms designed for singles, and a shared bathroom.

I hold Mum's hand. Mum feels her way. 'This is Dad's and my room. And this other room is Dad's office,' Mum tells me. 'And Dad's table.'

Small coffee table, covered with his papers. Walls cluttered with photo frames.

Mum goes out the door. Dad gestures for me to wait. We wait, and Mum comes back in through the second door. 'And this is Dad's office,' Mum tells me. 'And Dad's table. And there's another room,' Mum says. 'Show Pam your other room, Fred … Fred!' Mum feels along the wall. 'Show Pam the other room!'

'I've told you!' Dad says. 'There is no other room!'

'There is a room!'

'There is no room!' Dad knuckle-raps the wall. 'Can't you see? It's just a wall.'

'There is a room!' Mum clenches her hands, beats the wall. 'Show her, Fred!'

Dad's eyes flash frustration: he's caught a glimpse of the long and empty path that lies ahead. 'There is no room!'

'There is a room!' Mum goes for him, fingers clawed. 'I could stab you!'

'Keep your voice down!' Dad growls, catching her wrists. 'You're being silly.'

'Don't you dare talk to her like that!' I free Mum's hands, avoid Dad's eyes.

'Sit down here with me, Mum.' *Are you watching, Dad?* 'Come on, sweetheart.' I pat the bed. 'I'll show you.' I draw two squares. 'These are your rooms, Mum. See?' *Are you watching, Dad?* 'And this one here, the third one, is the bathroom, see the skylight? There's no other room, sweetheart, it's just the big mirror in the bathroom.'

'Dad's got it locked!' Mum sobs. 'Why won't you show Pam the other room?'

I don't know who that 'I could stab you!' woman was; I've never heard my mum raise her voice. *I could stab you!* Never seen my mum lose her temper—*I could stab you!*—and come at him like she meant it. That 'I could stab you!' woman's gone. It was only a fleeting visit. I'd like to tell you it was because she trusted me that there was no other room, but instead it was, 'That'd be right! You're all sticking up for your father ...' Dad has taken all the knives from the unit, but I don't imagine that the thought of waking up with a fork stuck in your eyeball is very restful.

My mum and I are holding hands in the back of Betty's station wagon. Betty has one hand in a packet of Allen's snakes and one hand on the wheel. Dad's pointing out who lives where, and who used to live over there before he/she died. And there's Bartlams Ltd, where Granny used to get loaded up with her weekly shop—Zara Clark Museum now.

We're heading out to the anabranch: trapped possums, '36; cut wood, '44; built a home '79. Turn off the highway. At a fork in the dirt road: 'Just stop for a tick, Betty. See that big bottle tree in that patch of scrub, Mum? Do you remember it?'

'No, love.'

'You remember, Mum! Blue threw me, and you got such a fright when you saw him galloping home without me, remember? I was hiding from a Brahman bull behind that tree, and you took that bull on in the Moke ...'

Jeannie and Clive are wonderful people: *We think of it as Fred and Olive's place; you can visit anytime you like.* Jeannie and Clive have done a wonderful job renovating; they've put a big deck overlooking the water. All the way down that steep bank are steps: *Fred and Olive, '94* engraved in the cement.

'This is where you had your turkeys, Mum. And this is where they shot a scene of stolen cattle in the film *The Irishman*, and this is where Dad found Peggy the pig and yak-yak-yakeddy-yak ...'

Here's Cactus, Lisa, Rosie, Cleo—the little cement tombstones Dad made for their various dogs along the way.

'You've done a wonderful job, thank you for letting us come.'

'We think of it as Fred and'—did her eyes slide away from Mum?—'Olive's place.'

Fletcherview is only three mile up the road. Betty pulls up under the flood marker Dad put up. We go over and I read the plaque to Mum:

This is the original site of Fletcherview, one of the earliest hotels in the district. In 1900 when Eva Brennan held the licence it was regarded as one of the most popular fishing spots along the Burdekin River. The Charters Towers Angling Club held many competitions at the nearby Big Rocks with Fletcherview as the weekend headquarters. In 1909 the licence was transferred to Charles and Annie Wheeler (Knuth). In 1924, Charles and Annie's daughter married Richard Chapman who later purchased the property and operated it as a cattle station.

After Richard's accidental death in 1945, May managed the property for almost 30 years until her death in 1974.

The 1946 record flood in the Burdekin rose over 7 feet in the upstairs storey.

The property now belongs to James Cook University. The buildings were sold for removal in 1987.

1987: Fred and Olive

Two record floods couldn't shift the homestead, but James Cook University could: nothing left at Fletcherview, just two big tanks up the back, and a crumbling chunk of cement—the remains of Granny's big cement block where she had her boiler.

Heading home, I'm holding Mum's hand. 'Turn it up, Betty.'

'Remember this song, Mum? Whitney Houston's "Greatest love of all".' I bring her hand to my lips. 'Don't you love it?'

I'm not only grieving for my mother; I'm grieving for a way of life that's gone under the hammer: *Sold!* to the highest bidder.

*

Anabranch: 1979

'There's a bull,' Mum says. 'Come through the fence from Fletcherview. Uncle Ian says just push that bull back down onto Big Sandy.'

My horse, Big Blue, is 16.1 hands high. When Blue's got a hump in his back, Blue's closer to 17 hands high, and you can count on Blue having a hump in his back whenever you girth him up. When Blue's got a hump in his back, Blue gets around on his toes, fartin' and startin', and lookin' like a camel.

Only Arab gene Blue got is colour and tail: no Arab in that ewe neck, big head and donkey ears. Blue usually gets around with his tail kinked over his back, but when Blue's pussyfooting on his toes, Blue holds that tail jammed tight between his legs. When Blue has his tail jammed and a hump in his back, the saddle is higher than my head, and the *last thing ya wanna do is stick a toe in Blue* when he's got a hump in his back and looking like a camel, so I lead him over to Dad's besser-block fence, and get on him from there.

Bought Blue from a mob of brumbies run in on Dawsonvale, and named him after Mum—but 'Oliver' didn't stick. People mostly called him 'big blue bastard' and 'Blue' stuck.

Blue *can unload ya* whenever he's got a mind to. Pony Club break-up I was awarded *Thrown Most Times in One Day* (six), but usually if you keep your feet well forward, and give 'im some rein—*not too much, but!*—and *don't jam 'im*, as Greg says, *yer can walk him off and kid him outta droppin' his nut*. I keep my feet well forward, and *give 'im some rein—not too much, but!*—and head off up the paddock.

What I *should* be doing is trotting him for half an hour before I try to *push that bull back down onto Big Sandy*, but what can you expect when the cricket's on? Thommo and Lillie were hammering the Poms with short-pitched deliveries kicking up head height at something like 100 mile per hour when I was having *a good rest* after finishing Grade Twelve. Now, I *need a good rest* because I've just finished my final year at uni, and everyone knows how hard you work at uni.

What I was best at was sculling. They have a big boat-race regatta every year down on the bottom oval. Teams of four or individual events—no one can beat me at sculling. Even boys can't beat me at sculling. No one can scull a ten-ounce beer faster than me. I'm not too bad at playing snooker either.

So it's good being at home. It's good lying around all day and afterwards having *a good rest, love.* 'Dad! You gotta come an' watch! Rod Marsh's got six dismissals! Dad ...' Reckon Uncle Ian should push his own damned bull back down onto Big Sandy. 'Dad! You gotta come an' watch! Thommo's battin' an' we still need nineteen runs to win.' I could be working in town but how can I get a job when I live eighteen kay outta town and don't own a car? Better to have *a good rest* lying on the carpet watching the cricket and sneaking Dad's scorched almonds.

I catch and saddle Blue. By the time I get to the fork in the road, Blue's not so humped, and the bull's only a few yards away from the gate into the bottom paddock. I go wide, the bull watching me, and open the gate. 'Go-orn!' I push Blue at him.

Bulls are supposed to paw the ground first, but this one hasn't read the handbook. No warning, he's coming straight at me. I spin Blue and hook him. Blue drops his nut. I'm halfway down Blue's side and see that patch of scrub and bottle tree coming at me; grab a limb; momentum barks my hands and wrists and thumps me on hands and knees.

Blue's gone: Blue's pig-jumping, stirrups flapping, down towards the house.

Now that bull rakes up dirt. *Now* that bull has his head down, raking up dirt and circling my tree. *Can't outrun him.* I'm circling my tree too. *Just have to wait him out.*

I hear the Moke coming: Mum, speeding down the road. Mum's seen Blue come home—riderless. Mum sees the bull circling me hiding behind my tree. Mum revs the Moke at him.

Bull spins, charges. Bluffs. Mum brakes.

'Mum!' I yell, waving her away. 'Leave 'im, Mum! He's no good.'

Ladies and gentlemen, in the green corner, weighing in at 450 kilos, it's Mum and Smokin-Mokin'! In the red corner, firin' up at 1000 kilos, IT'S MAD-BULL 'KNOCKOUT' BRAHMAN.

'Get outta here, Mum! Get out!'

Mad-bull swings his head, eyeballs me: *You'll keep.* Mad-bull eyeballs the Moke: *But I'm gonna 'ave you!* Mad-bull rakes dirt: *Gonna squash ya like a bug!* Dust billows above hump and lowered head.

Engine revs.

'Muuuum! Back … off!'

Mum'n Smokin-Mokin' jam reverse, slam first, charge …

But here comes MAD-BULL 'KNOCKOUT' BRAHMAN!

No bluff this time: Mad-bull crashes his big head into the grille, and is ramming the Moke backwards. *Mad-bull's got a horn stub hooked under the bumper! Smokin-Mokin's in reverse, engine whining!*

Moke's front-wheel drive and both front wheels are off the ground.

'Muuum!'

Bumper slips off horn. Moke thumps down. Mum bounces. Spinning wheels spray dirt, gain traction. *Smokin-Mokin cuts a semicircle—backwards—at full throttle.* 'Get in!' Mum yells, and we're careering down the track, side-swiping saplings.

Breathe out, look back. 'He's stopped; he's not coming.' Breathe in. 'Slow down, Mum!' Breathe out. 'Before you kill us both.'

Mum brakes at the house fence.

I exhale. 'You stupid, stupid woman! What were you thinking!'

Mum inhales. 'Thinkin' I didn't wanna see *you* mashed by a bull! That damned Ian!' Mum's heading for the phone. 'He knew that bull was rogue.'

'You don't know that!'

'I know your Uncle Ian!' Mum picks up the phone. 'I've got a good mind to give him a piece of mine!'

I'm trotting Blue in circles, have taken the hump out of him when I see Uncle Ian and Richard coming in their new Toyota, red cattle dog in the back.

Uncle Ian winds down the window, grins. 'Had a bit of trouble, did you?'

Richard's grown into that big cowboy hat, but the silly grin on Richard's face makes me wish I hadn't taken the hump out of Blue before he got on.

Dog's grinning too. Dog jumps down, tail wagging, says to Blue, *How ya doin', big boy? Name's Red.* Red knows there's something more than bulldust in the wind.

Richard sizes up my hunting pad, thinks better of it, takes a big stock saddle from the back of the Toyota. Uncle Ian hands up a stockwhip, same stockwhip Granny Chapman chased Dough-arse and Richie with round the toilet block—*You boys gonna git what youse got comin'!*—and a bag of rocks?

'We'll git 'im.' Uncle Ian's eyebrows twitch. 'Just gotta know how to handle 'em.'

Richard and Blue on one flank, and Red—*we'll git 'im*—slinking in on the other, Uncle Ian pushes the Toyota at the bull.

Mad-bull charges, side-swipes the Cruiser.

That bull is goin' out—dead or alive!

*

Charters Towers: July 2010

'Do you remember, Mum? Blue was dripping sweat, and the new Toyota had a big dint on the driver's door, and the other door wouldn't open ...' Arm in arm, we're walking, walking, walking.

'You remember: you got a big fright when you saw Blue come home without me and—'

'That damned Ian,' Mum says. 'He knew that bull was rogue.'

'You do remember, Mum! You do—'

'I need to pee!'

'Okay, Mum.' I take her hand. 'This way, sweetheart.'

Dad's sitting at his desk, head cupped in hands. Lips moving silently, he's proofing another letter to the editor, advocating euthanasia. He doesn't look up.

'This way, Mum. Turn around now. Turn around. Let's get these slacks down … don't sit down yet, love. We have to take these ones down too.'

Mum reaches for the railing; her other hand clings to mine as she lowers her bottom.

As I listen to the sound of her trickling water … stop … start again … stop, Whitney Houston fills the vacant spaces in my head.

'Don't stand up yet, Mum. We have to wipe first.'

Mum looks all around.

'Here you go, sweetheart.' I pull paper from the roll, fold it, hand it.

Mum takes it. Looks at it. Looks up at me.

'Down here, darling.' I touch her inner thigh. 'We wipe down here, remember?'

And she does.

'No, no, sweetheart! We don't put it back on the roll … drop it, Mum … in the toilet. That's the way. Good girl! Come on now, let's stand up. Panties up like this. There you go. Slacks up, and then we flush. Ready to go?'

'Yes, thank you, love.'

'Out here, sweetie. We'll wash our hands … here, under the tap … that's the way.' I wipe her hands, kiss her temple. 'You're such a good girl, aren't you?'

Mum looks at me, sees me. '*You're* a good girl! How do you know these things? Who taught you all these things?'

'You did, Mum.' I hold her to me. 'You taught me all these things.'

11

Anger management 101

Anyone can become angry—that is easy. But to be angry with the right person, to the right degree, at the right time, for the right purpose, and in the right way—this is not so easy.

Aristotle

Charters Towers, Eventide: October 2010

Phone call: Pammie? I want you to come and take me home! Now! Tonight!

Me: I can't come tonight, darling girl. Remember, I live in New South Wales—

Mum: Well. That's that then! Thought I could at least rely on you!

Me: Mum, I'll be there in two days … Mum …

Dad: No use talking to her.

Dad's playing his accordion and Gene Autry: 'That silver-haired daddy of mine'.

I peer through the louvres: Mum is still asleep.

From his chair, Cokie smiles broadly. *Easier to leave her sleeping, isn't it?*

I open the door against a pair of pull-ups heavy with pee. The room smells.

Mum's on her back, head a little crooked on the pillow. Her dark hair, streaked with silver, lies flattened in several wrong directions. Doona thrown back, mattress is patched by darker shades of damp; sheets lie crumpled on the floor. My mum is lying on that smelly bed looking up at me like a little girl who knows that she's been naughty.

'Hello, sweetheart.' I drop the nappy in the bin, stick my head next door. 'Hey!'

Dad reaches for his stick, tries to stand, wobbles.

'Don't get up, Fred. Just letting you know I'm here.'

'We had a bad night.' He sinks back down. 'Take care of your mother, would you?'

No passive immersion in sadness for my dad. My dad's got a mission and a red gopher. He hoons around town on his red gopher at full throttle. One time, my dad's straw hat blew off. He tried to catch his hat and ran the front wheel onto the kerb *and rolled it*. There's my dad and his red gopher lying in the middle of the highway. *Good thing some man came along and not a semitrailer!*

I sewed some elastic in his hat, so now it won't blow off.

Mum used to follow Dad around on her red gopher …

Dad only takes me away from Mum when he's got *too much to carry* or has *places to go, people to see*. When Dad has places to go, people to see, we park Mum down at Betty's shop and I park Betty's car—*as close as I can, Dad*—near people and places.

'Hello, Mr Bagnall. Do you have something new for us?'

174

'Oh, just a few bit and pieces.' He waves his cuttings at the librarian. 'But only if you're interested.'

'Of course we're interested.' She pushes her chair back. 'Come on, I'll help you.'

Cuttings in one hand, walking stick in the other, Fred Bagnall follows her. My dad's slightly stooped, walks with the shortened step of an aged person. *What do you expect, silly bitch—he's ninety-four!*

If you ever happen to visit the Charters Towers Excelsior Library, you'll see the 'Fred Bagnall Alcove': Fred Bagnall's three books, and years and years of his newspaper clippings in clear plastic folders.

Above the desk is a huge, hand-drawn charcoal portrait of Mr Fred Bagnall.

Fred Bagnall, glasses perched on his crooked nose, Founding Father of the Nation: wise, compassionate—clearly a Man of Vision.

Fred Bagnall can't see past the end of that crooked nose!

Negative voice in running commentary: *Mum spent every waking moment taking care of you: cold compresses, hot compresses and hot water bottles. Every kind of back support known to man.* 'I'll just nip down to the chemist and get a good tonic for you, Fred; Liney Russell'll know what's good, Fred.' *Ear drops, eye drops, throat drops.* 'Bed socks for your feet, love; beanie for your head, love.' *Bandaging, bathing, massaging, soothing:* 'An' a good tonic from Liney down at the chemist.'

'Hello, Pam!' The librarian reads polite blankness. She has the advantage: she's recognised Fred Bagnall; I'm the 'and daughter'.

'Toni!' Toni says. 'Toni Pritchard.'

'I'm so sorry to hear about your mother,' I say. 'Betty only told me this morning.'

'It was a blessing,' Toni chatters on. 'Severe strokes ...'

All I hear is: *blessing*. Blessing? Blessing!

She's smiles beatifically. '... weeks in hospital, so, in the end, it was a blessing.'

I hate her. On what planet is it a 'blessing' when your mother dies?

Dad's mission today is letters to the editor of every newspaper in Queensland.

'Why won't they publish them? Not one damned paper!'

'I don't know, Dad. People just don't want to talk about it.'

'Why not? Death! It's just a part of living. Why's everyone so afraid?'

'I don't know, Dad.'

Dad corners me at every opportunity with clippings: WHY CAN'T WE MAKE OUR OWN CHOICES?; DR NITSCHKE'S DEATH DIY; WHEN IT'S TIME …

'Read this!' Big finger pokes a clipping on the table. 'Read this! When you take sleeping pills, it's best to put a plastic bag over your head to make sure—'

'That's disgusting, Dad!'

'I know it's disgusting! So why won't they talk about it? Not one damned paper!'

'Perhaps if you made it personal, Dad? Write about'—*and think about!*—'all the wonderful things you've done together, and don't just focus on the negative?'

'I might just do that. Yes, I might just do that.'

Dear Sir,

My wife Olive and I have had a wonderful life together.

For well over sixty years we have chosen our homes, our workplaces and our friends. We have chosen our pets, our motor vehicles, our sports and our hobbies.

We have chosen our holidays together. We have crossed Australia on the *Indian Pacific*, and gone down to Melbourne on the *Spirit of Progress*. We have flown through the Grand Canyon—and I flew the plane. We have swum at the bottom of Wallaman Falls and watched the sun set over Cable Beach. We have flown over Lake Eyre and climbed Ayers Rock. We have taken photos of the large rocks at the bottom of the British Empire. We have lunched at the top of Sydney Tower and paddled under 19 bridges on the River Avon in New Zealand.

But now our life is over! Oh, we're still here, but our quality of life is over. This is certainly no reflection on Eventide … But why can't we choose the time and place of our last journey together and legally die with dignity??

Fred Bagnall, Charters Towers, QLD

I watch Dad sitting at his table, head cupped, lips moving silently. When Robyn died Dad wandered around saying, 'Robyn was the lucky one, Robyn had a way out!' Now, he's started saying it again: *Robyn had a way out!* If Dad ever said Robyn was the lucky one in front of Greg, Greg would deck him.

If Dad mentions plastic bags again, I'll deck him.

'Here, sweetheart, they don't go over your head; we put our feet in here. That's the way. And we'll put our teeth in before we go.'

Every day we walk. Every day I wave and smile: *Good morning, Mrs Watlow.*

Every day we walk: *Hello, Tom, Dick and Harry.*

Every day, sitting outside their little units, they wave and smile— watching me walk my late mother to her postponed appointment with death.

There are five sets of units with cement paths running between them. Lots of paths and lots of places to walk. 'Where are you going, Mum?' It was easier when I could read to her. 'Just going for a walk, love.' Easier when she didn't mind walking with me. 'No, love, you don't have to follow me around all day! You all think I'm stupid, and I'm not stupid!'

Now, I walk a few metres behind her. *You won't be able to catch her if she falls!* 'Morning, Mrs Western.' *But I can catch up if she's heading for stairs or the main gate.* 'Hello, Tom, Dick and ... Goodbye, Harry.'

Some days, the Rec. Officer organises little get-togethers. But my mum can't play cards—she doesn't recognise the suits. My mum can't play bingo—she doesn't recognise the numbers. My mum doesn't watch *Days of Our Lives* anymore, but sometimes she'll *have a little lie-down* in the afternoon.

When Mum goes to sleep, I start flicking channels: *The Doctors* tell me that during menopause a woman's metabolic rate can fall by 40 per cent; if I lose just ten pounds, I can cut my risk of diabetes by a whopping 60 per cent! If I take the drug Avandia I have a 43 per cent chance of having a heart attack. Flick. *Dr Oz* tells me prunes are now called dried plums; a recent survey has shown that ... Flick. Tail end of a panel of experts: elegant African American, petite Asian and fat Caucasian doing a survey, on two women in the audience, on whether it's better to be a short woman or a tall woman, before moving on to:

African American: A recent survey has shown that many women are now more turned on by pictures of shopping than pictures showing sex acts.

Petite Asian: Women don't respond to porn; not like men do.

Fat Caucasian: Women who have sex twice a week—now listen carefully, girls! Women who have sex twice a week have 50 per cent less chance of dying, when compared to women who have sex only once a month.'

Wankers! No wonder Elvis shot his TV set.

Dr Phil: No one makes *mistakes* anymore; we make *poor choices*. No matter what, no matter how reprehensible—so long as we talk about it. We are a soul-shirking, pain-avoiding, old-age-defying, death-denying culture. *Take one three times a day* has become reams of computerised pharmacological information—enough to send you blind, if not scare you half to death. I open my eyes. I'd drifted off. Mum's gone.

I bolt outside. Thank God! Catch up.

'You're a lovely girl,' Mum says. 'But where's your mother?'

'You're my mother, Mum.'

'That's a lovely thing to say.' Mum pats my hand. 'But I mean your real mother, love, where's she?'

'You are my mother, Mum.' I stop, face her. 'Look at me!'

'Didn't your real mother want you?'

'Mum.' I take her face between my hands. 'It's me, Mum. It's Pam.'

She shakes her head. 'Pammie rings me every day.'

'I know, Mum. I ring you every day.'

'No, another Pam,' Mum says. 'She rings me every day.'

I know, Mum. Pam-jack-in-the-box: 'It's me!'

I'm remembering how Mum used to write to me, every week. I have her last letter. It's a small page with spidery scrawl meandering up and down. It's mostly indecipherable, but you can pick out a few words and phrases here and there: *fence … horses … I loved every minute …* And the sign-off line: *you are the sunshine*. At least, I think that's what it says.

'Where are you going, Mum?'

'I've got to be getting home now.'

'You are home, Mum.' I take her hand. 'See, Dad's up there on the veranda?'

'I want to go home,' Mum says. 'Mum will be wondering where I am.'

'Darling girl, come with me.'

'It's getting dark.' Mum twists away. 'And there might be snakes along the way.'

Dad catches my eye: *See! See what I have to put up with?*

'Come on, sweetheart. Let's have a shower, before tea?'

Mum cries. 'I want … to go … home!'

'Sweetheart,' I promise. 'I'll walk all the way home with you, when it's time. But we should have a shower now. And later, you can hop into bed with Dad. Remember?'

AT EVENTIDE a person may be assessed as requiring Residential Care if that person's physical, mental or social functioning is affected to such a degree that the person cannot maintain himself or herself independently without support.

Eventide Manual

'Put your hand here, Mum. Hang on to the bar. Lift this arm, now this one, that's a good girl. Turn around, doesn't that feel good?'

'I wanna go home! Why can't I go home? I don't like it here.'

Hollow voice fills hollow silence: 'Why don't you like it here, sweetheart?'

'There's a little girl thinks I'm stupid follows me around all day.'

A nurse taps at the screen door.

'I'll see you in the morning, sweetheart.'

'He's got another room in there.' Mum tells me as we hug. 'He's got it locked.'

'See what I have to put up with every day?' Dad turns the volume down. 'Every day this happens.'

'I know, Dad.' I step outside. 'See you in the morning.'

Dad turns the volume up. Hank Thompson: 'The blackboard of my heart'.

Outside, a mouldy, raggedy clown leans back in a veranda chair. From this angle, you can't see the jagged hole in his head.

What you looking at? Cokie asks.

'Nothing,' I tell Cokie. 'I'm looking at nothing.'

Ah! Cokie nods his broken head. *Don't think about it; don't dwell on it. You sidestep it but it's always there, walking parallel—one step behind you, one step in front—but there, just the same.*

'Fuck off, Cokie.'

Good girls don't swear! Swearing is uncouth!

'Yeah, well …'

It's hard, loving someone by phone—harder still when they don't know who you are.

*

People with dementia fall more often. Over time, it becomes increasingly difficult for them to report pain and injury.

Christmas Eve 2010

Phone call: Can you come up the coast road? Mum's in Townsville Hospital.

Me: What happened, Betty?

Betty: She had a little fainting turn. Don't worry, she wasn't hurt.

Me: But why did they take her to Townsville Hospital?

Betty: Regulations.

'Does it hurt, sweetheart?' I kiss Mum's hand.

Poor little girl, propped up on pillows. Poor little broken face, black and purple.

'She's just drowsy.' A nurse pats my mum's shoulder. 'Okay, Olive?'

Get away from her!

'You're okay now, aren't you, Olive?' The nurse turns to me. 'Just the pain medication. She'll be discharged as soon as the doctor does his rounds.'

Smash your face! 'Why was she brought to Townsville?' *Bash your face!*

'Regulation. Observation after a fall.'

'But she wasn't hurt!' *Stomp your face, till it looks like hers!* 'Why bring her here?'

'Regulation. Doctor will be along shortly.'

But she wasn't hurt! Betty said she wasn't hurt! 'Where did this happen?' *Poor little broken face; poor smashed face all black and purple.*

'First bed. Just around the corner. She must've tried to climb out.'

Regulation says: *Hospital bed is hip high.*

Regulation says: *Bars up!*

Regulation says: *Cold floor, hard linoleum.*

My mum, waking in the middle of the night, lost, alone … climbing over those bars … smashing her face on cold, hard floor— from chest height!

Was she frightened in the middle of the night? Lost, climbing over those bars?

How much does it hurt, smashing an eye socket on cold, hard floor?

Dull blue iris in a pool of blood asks, 'Can I go home now, love?'

'Just as soon as the doctor comes, Mum.'

At Eventide, I lead my mum up towards their unit. Dad's waiting on the veranda. He takes in Mum's poor smashed face, scowls, shakes his head, goes into the other room.

'It would be better if she'd gone, that day she fainted up on Buckland's Hill.'

'Keep your voice down, Dad! We don't know if or when she might be listening.'

Dad makes a definitive gesture. *I don't want to talk about it.*

I watch Mum sleeping. Without memory it must be like talking to yourself when there's no one there. I wonder, too, what words mean to my mum. I imagine words are like fireflies: evanescent little spheres of meaning peripheral to a shrinking pool or light. If she were to call her 'self' would that 'self' recognise her name?

Is she dreaming?

Can she dream?

There's a firefly ...

Trembling in the corner of her eye ...

If she could see that little firefly, it would trip from her tongue.

Only ... she remembers ... water ... and pink and purple ... and pink and purple. Waterlilies! Ah, yes, she has it now: pink and purple waterlilies on water.

Waterlilies! And a flock of gadding fireflies: gentle black hands, laughter rippling on water. She can see them now, children playing in the water. Mummy ... waiting up there in the shade ... and she remembers ...

'Mum?'

She'll stay here. She likes it here. Here, on this strand of waking dreams, the world makes sense.

'Does it hurt, Mum?'

Why, then, must the world wake up and make no sense at all?

'No, it doesn't hurt, love.' Mum gives a little smile. 'Can I go home now?'

*

Charters Towers, Eventide: July/August 2011

Dad's playing his accordion and Hank Williams: 'I'm so lonesome I could cry'.

I peer through the louvres: Mum is still asleep.

Easier to leave her sleeping, isn't it?

'Fuck off, Cokie.'

Cokie smiles broadly. *Thought you only swear with your mates?*

'Yeah, well …'

Bedroom stinks. 'Don't get up, Fred. Just letting you know I'm here.'

'We had a bad night.' He sinks back down. 'Take care of your mother, would you?'

Doona thrown back; mattress patched by darker shades of damp; sheets, soiled pink nightie and soaked panties lie crumpled on the floor.

My mum, in singlet and padded panties … so tiny … so precious, I could …

What? Put her in your bellybutton? Keep her safe?

She's sleeping, mouth slightly open. I stand, for a long time, listening to the soft sounds of her breathing. And the words come: *Please, God, let her go!*

Then my mum is looking up at me like a little girl who knows she's been naughty.

Oh, Mum.

'Hello, sweetheart.' I sit down beside her. 'How are you?'

'I'm sorry.' My mum, lying in a smelly bed, faded eyes distracted. 'I'm so sorry.'

'You're a silly chook!' I lean down, kiss her cheek. 'You've nothing to be sorry for, sweetheart. But let's get you up and dressed, and then you can come down to the laundry and help me do some washing.'

I help her up, lead her into the toilet, pull the panties down—and track sloppy poop down her legs. 'Sit down, Mum. I'll get these off. Lift this foot. Now this one. Yucky pooh!' I joke, trying not to gag. 'Who's got a poopy bum?'

Mum giggles. 'You are wicked!' Then my mum is laughing like Mum used to laugh—at herself, at me. We laugh together, ridiculously, foolishly together.

I cradle her head against my stomach, backhand my eyes.

Fred hears us, calls out, 'Why the mirth?'

'Nothing, Dad,' I call back. 'I just said something silly.'

Mum's laughter fades. She looks up at me. 'Oh, Pammie,' she murmurs. Faded eyes fading into sadness, she hangs her head. 'Why on earth do you have to put up with this?'

She knows me! Heart sings. Soul soars. *My mother knows me!*

'I'm not putting up with anything.' I lift her face, thumb away her tears. 'I love you, Mum.'

She touches my cheek. 'I know you do, love.'

*

10 August 2011 11.37AM AEST

ABC: EXISTING, NOT LIVING
By Nathalie Fernbach

Charters Towers author and newspaper columnist Fred Bagnall is a man on a mission—he's trying to get permission to end his own life and the life of his wife Olive.

What would you imagine a man wanting to die to be like?

Fred Bagnall is not what I expected.

The 94-year-old author and newspaper columnist is animated as he rifles through paperwork and articles scattered on his

185

dining table, explaining his campaign to seek permission to end his own life.

'The response to any letters I have written to the premier of the state is "no, they will not allow euthanasia". So I have either got to put up with what I have got now or commit murder suicide and I can't do that.'

*

September 2011

WELCOME TO EVENTIDE: NURSING HOME—HIGH CARE SECTION. This section of Eventide caters for people who need continuous nursing care, not just supervision and help with daily tasks. There are four separate living areas—Pandanus, Raintree, Tamarind and Waratah.

Eventide Manual

'Come on.' RN puts the phone down. 'I'll take you.'

I follow her down a broad avenue: male toilet, female toilet, library, games room.

'We like the family to make the decision. We've been waiting for someone to come.' *And I've come. I'm your Judas.* 'It's way past due. She might be hit by a car ... or the food trolley. We'd have made the decision ourselves soon anyway. Olive's severely demented and ...' *That's my mum you're talking about!*

I turn my head away, nod ... nod ... nodding that I understand.

'It'll take a few weeks for the paperwork—'

'Why?' *Nod, nod, nod.* Yes, I understand we have to wait for an expert to come from Townsville to *ascertain that Olive's severely demented.*

Up ahead, yellow bars of a six-foot fence surround carefully tended lawns.

'Have a good look around.' She swipes a card. 'Head will talk to you when she can.'

AT RAINTREE we have communal areas for entertainment, television and relaxing.

Eventide Manual

A man's abandoned brown slipper lying on the floor; general sense of busyness: nurses and orderlies leading, cajoling, coaxing shambling figures in pyjamas and dressing-gowns.

At least it's bright. Walls are white or cream; sunshine spilling into a windowed reception room that faces east.

'Yarrrh! Yarrrh!' A cool and palely soft hand catches my elbow. 'Yarrh! Yarrh!' A middle-aged boy looks up at me from beneath the brim of a khaki army hat. 'Yarrh?'

'It's not walk time, Bobby.' An orderly unlatches the hand. 'Time for breakfast.'

Bobby's wearing a flannel shirt unbuttoned, trackpants skew-whiff, and one jelly sandal. When God was making Bobby, God didn't leave the face in the kiln long enough: Bobby's face has sloughed to one side. 'Yarrrrrhhhhhh!' Bobby's in his forties. Bobby was 'born that way'. Bobby's been institutionalised all his life. Bobby will spend the next ten, twenty, thirty years *Yarrh! Yarrhing* his way around Raintree.

'Help me! Help me!' A long, low moan is coming down a corridor. 'They're going to take me away. They're going to murder me!' An ancient gypsy fortune teller—escaped from the pages of *Tales Beyond Midnight*—looks up at me. 'Help me!' With one eye screwed shut, she chews her lip. 'They're coming to take me away!'

'Come on, Malka. Breakfast time, love.'

AT RAINTREE residents are provided with opportunities to explore their own abilities with sensitivity ...

Eventide Manual

The Rec. Officer has been busy. Each door down the corridor sports a colourful hand-drawn name: *Ashley's Room*; *Alec's Room*. An arts and crafts table in one corner boasts a box of plasticine: red rage, pink love, happy yellow. As a kid, you tried to keep those colours separate, but somehow always ended up with an ugly, big grey glob.

The front glass doors slide open as I approach. And I can see my Mum walking through those doors as often as she pleases. It's beautiful outside. There's a white birdcage to the left of the door; yellow and blue budgerigars are chirping in the morning sun. There's a blue sail strung from a paperbark tree; in the fork, just out of reach, a bob-tailed tortoiseshell cat watches me with curious yellow eyes as I *have a good look around*. There are tables and chairs on the veranda, and along a bricked path another patio set beneath a big maroon umbrella.

It's a bright and brilliant sunny day. I follow the path to where an open gate lets me into another enclosure. Could be anyone's backyard; it's inviting: four cane tables and chairs here, shaded by a big blue sail. *Me and my mum sitting here, drinking tea.*

I follow the path to where the garden narrows and I'm walking with the yellow bars on one side. *Every person should be encouraged to make decisions concerning their daily living and be provided with support to maximise their independence.* Around the corner, I find another garden. There's a red telephone box, a railway siding, and a raised wooden box planted with cherry tomatoes. And there's a little white-and-tan terrier, a patient puppy, snoozing in the tomato bed. 'You're going to love it, Dad! There's a dog and a vegie patch.' (And a six foot fence.) 'And you won't have to worry about Mum anymore.'

There's a shock of grey hair, a hooked nose and a pair of shaggy eyebrows, lying under the mango tree. I'll learn soon enough that it's Ashley. Ashley's neck and back have fused. Age has made an S-bend out of Ashley, but, look closely, you'll find the remnants of a strapping, handsome man. Ashley is a walker. Ashley's wearing one brown slipper. Ashley's wearing flannel pyjama pants hitched up, knotted under his armpits. When Ashley's not walking, Ashley's lying on the lawn. Tears running down his face, Ashley prays: 'Our Father, who art in Heaven, hallowed be thy name. Our Father ...'

'It's not all roses here, you know?'

There's a big woman watching me watch Ashley. T-shirt, grey work pants, heavy boots, dark complexion, wire fringe jutting above black eyebrows above black eyes. She's been brought in from hunting polar bears, or clubbing white baby seals on the ice. Wonder where she parked her huskies?

She raises a hand—to me? Other hand holds a silver ring heavy with multiple keys.

'You must be Pam?' she says. 'Come in. Your mum and dad's room won't be ready for a few days, but I'll show you around the rest of the facility and grounds.'

I've already seen the rest of the facility and the grounds. I follow her anyway.

Dad has visitors sitting at the table on the veranda outside their unit. Relatives—Chapmans—from Eidsvold, where my Granddad Dick came from.

Hello, hello. How are you?

I look through the louvres. Mum's asleep in singlet and padded panties.

'I'll just go down to the dining room, Dad,' I say, as I put mouldy old Cokie out of the way under the table. 'Get some extra cups and plates.'

Coming back along the veranda, I see my mum. She's finding her way out through the screen door. She's found her way into a shirt and a pair of my dad's underpants, pulled up over her nappy.

Mum sits down and smiles. Their eyes slide off Mum. They talk to Dad. *Yak-yak-yakeddy-yak.*

'Come on,' I whisper. 'Come with me, sweetheart.'

Mum comes like the good little girl she is, and always has been.

When I bring Mum back outside, *yak-yak-yakeddy-yak*, their eyes slide right off her again. They talk to Dad. *Yak-yak-yakeddy-yak.* 'Goodbye. So nice to see you. Goodbye.'

A nurse comes to help Olive with her shower. It's not her job. At the units, inmates are supposed to be self-sufficient but Raintree's paperwork is going to take some time.

I put Cokie on the table, and wait for the sound of dinner coming.

Eh-hum! He clears his throat. *Can't wait for the sound of dinner coming, can you?*

I ignore him. Dinner comes at five o'clock. Dinner comes in a steel cabinet pulled behind a little motor cab. Every afternoon, I wait for the sound of dinner coming.

Feeling a little sorry for yourself?

'Can it, Cokie! You have no idea how I feel.'

Let me guess: you saw yourself sailing to Byzantium, hiking in Peru, but here you are, up shit creek in a barbed-wire canoe?

'Without a paddle. And it wasn't a creek; it was more like a slime pond.'

Who's telling this story?

'Not me, that's for sure.'

Life … Cokie slumps and sighs. *Perhaps it's time you saw it as it really is?*

'Which is?'

190

Why, each story is but a funeral march: a slow procession to the grave. An undertaking, as it were, for which you did not volunteer, and over which you have no control, and for which there is only one possible conclusion. And, if you don't mind me saying, Pammie, you're old enough now to know that these things happen.

'I don't want to be a grown-up.'

You prefer the child's version? Cokie brightens. *Well, once upon a time there was a very naughty little boy. Whenever Mrs Almighty called out: 'What are you up to now?' Mrs Almighty knew he'd been up to no good, because as Mrs Almighty always said: 'That God! He's such a little prick!'*

'Now you're talking.'

So, this day, when Mrs Almighty calls, 'God! What are you up to now?' God's taking a piss on all the little creatures hell-bent on paddling out of a slime pond. Little prick's spent all morning kickin' 'em back, flickin' 'em back, and now the little prick's pissin' 'em back into the slime pond. 'You're such a little prick!' Mrs Almighty scolds. 'And you shouldn't be playing with it all the time, God, it'll send you blind.' But, squatting by the slime pond, God sees all the mashed and mangled little corpses he's stomped on, pissed on, and jacked off into the slime pond. And God saw that it was GOOD!

'You do know, don't you, Cokie?'

Cokie shrugs. *God's good at throwaway lines—and people.*

'You know and understand exactly how I feel.'

I know that stories don't have to make sense, deliver a moral—or have a happy ending. Cokie's smiling, but those Irish eyes are sad. *And I understand that it's soul destroying, watching a human tragedy as each day grinds on remorselessly.*

'It's like … we're all living in some sort of depressive realism.'

Boys will be boys. Cokie spreads his hands. *And you can't blame the little prick: poor little prick's got nothing but time on his hands; poor little prick has nothing else—and no one else—to play with.*

Nurse goes. *Thank you so much.*

Mum appears at the screen door. She comes outside, closes the door carefully behind her. She shuffles over to the second door, opens it, goes inside, closes the door carefully behind her. A minute later, she appears at the screen door. She comes outside, closes the door carefully behind her. She shuffles to the second door, opens it, goes inside, closes it carefully behind her. A minute later, she appears at the screen door. She comes outside, closes the door carefully behind her. She shuffles to the second door, opens it, goes inside, closes it carefully. A minute later, Mum appears at the screen door ...

See? Cokie whispers. *It's all exits and entrances...*

'Come here, darling,' I say to my mum. 'Come and sit with me for a minute.'

Mum sits down. I pull my chair to face hers. Knees touching, I take her hands, look into her face. 'How are you, sweetheart? Tell me what you've been doing.'

For the first time in a long time, she tries to make eye contact. Her sunken eyes search mine, and I wonder what she's thinking. What those failing eyes are seeing.

'Talk to me.' My mum is in there, somewhere. 'Tell me what you're doing.'

'I'm dying.'

Heart sinks. I stroke her hands.

Eyes tormented, she accuses me: 'I'm dying, aren't I?'

Soul shrinks. *Please, God, let her forget her question.* I stroke her hands.

Her eyes search my face. Her expressionless face reflects no inner peace, just the slow sense of the dying going on within.

I lean forward, rest my head in her lap. She falls to stroking my hair.

We wait for the sound of dinner coming.

'There's the dinner trolley coming, Mum. Fred!' I call. 'Dinner trolley's here!' I kiss my mum. 'I'll see you in the morning, love.'

Dad shuffles out, puts a big hand on her tiny shoulder. I watch as they head off together along the veranda to the dining room.

'Do you think she forgot her question, Cokie?'

Cokie smiles broadly, but his eyes are bright with tears. *Hope so.*

'He wouldn't do it?' I ask Cokie. 'He wouldn't, would he?'

Cokie's answer is emphatic: *Never!*

'I'm sorry I threw you in the bin, Cokie.'

Cokie shrugs. *C'est la vie.*

*

Betty's down the back in her granny flat getting *Spiritual Relief and Relaxation* with a psychic and some women friends. I'm here on Betty's front veranda getting *spiritual relief and relaxation* with a bottle of gin.

On the way home, Betty and I had words. Not an argument. Just words:

'Why can't he be nice to her?'

'Give it a rest, Pam. He's ninety-four.'

'Yes, but—'

'You come home for a few weeks at a time; he lives it every day.'

'Yes, but—'

'He's going down to Raintree with her; what more do you expect?'

I expect him to hold her, hug her.

Have you ever seen him hold her, hug her? Ever?

No, but—

No, but this is different ...

Betty and Bill live on a ten-acre block. Betty and Bill's two girls are overseas. Billie's at the Running of the Bulls in Pamplona, and Lesley's somewhere in Israel.

Sun's going down, and it's good to put your feet up on the railing and listen to cicadas sing. Mad Hatter, Bob Katter, lives just over there. And, as Bob Katter said, 'Without … Fred Bagnall, *The Irishman* might never have been filmed in Charters Towers.' Bob Katter's got a paddock of mango trees drooping in fatigue; Bob Katter's got: *no right not to take my calls! Bloody politicians! What are we paying them for? They're supposed to represent us!*

I know, Dad, but it's a very grey area.

Bloody Catholics! Why should they dictate my life? You support me, don't you?

Yes, I do. Yes, I'd help you take your life—if it came to that, but—
You'd do that? You'd help me?

Yes, but …

Yes, but: 'The patient must, of his own free will and at his own initiative, clearly and repeatedly request to die rather than continue suffering.'

Dad's been on sleeping pills ever since I've known him. Dad has his stash. And I have this romantic notion of taking him out to the Fletcher River where he wants to go to die. *There I am, holding his hand, and with his dying breath he'll know—he'll finally admit—that I'm okay after all.*

A shrink would probably tell me: *A father who has withheld approval binds the child in intractable ways.* I'd tell the shrink: *Aw, grow up, would'ja!*

Simultaneously involved and detached, I listen to him expressing outrage over the indignities that lie ahead, and the fear of losing control of his own life: he wants to know *how* and *when* and *where*. But, pills at hand, he needs us to agree that euthanasia is a 'good death', not an irrational act of suicide.

Look! You're not the scriptwriter here!

That's the paradox inherent in defeating death in this way: death still wins.

Being party to a 'good death' is said to be redemptive. I don't know what 'redemptive' means—unless it's a synonym for 'shattering'.

Robyn was the lucky one; Robyn had a way out.

Robyn *visited* Betty. Robyn didn't *visit* me. Robyn didn't *visit* her husband, Greg—even though Greg's 'seen the light'. Years ago, Greg got arsenic poisoning from cattle dip. He remembers hovering above them—the doctors, Robyn and his daughters—while they discussed his demise; says he was floating towards the light, and feeling good about it, when he was told he had to come back.

Robyn didn't *visit* Dad.

Does Dad know I'm angry with him?

A shrink might say: *Women—some women—are still bound by tradition: taught to mask feelings; taught to suppress anger and pretend to have feelings they don't have.*

I'd tell the shrink: *Live a lie long enough, you become one.*

A shrink might say: *Prolonged emotional distress creates neural static and can cripple rational thought. It is empathy and hope that keep distress from swamping rational thought.*

I'd tell the shrink: *Fred Bagnall's never been much at empathy, and we have no reason to hope.*

I put Cokie in the bin today. Said he didn't want to go to Raintree. Said he was tired—and sick and tired of living with a hole in his head. Said he wanted to go home.

Goodbye, Cokie. Nice knowing you.

It's a long way to Tipperary …

It's getting late. Sun has gone. Only sound is cicadas' night-time song.

I listen to night rhythms and underlying dissonant harmonies.

The cicada emerges from the ground to sing every summer. She only lives long enough to attract a mate with her song and complete the life cycle. When she moults, only the abandoned exoskeleton remains still clinging to the bark of trees. As kids, riding along

Lolworth, we used to collect them. Their tiny feet have hooks, so they cling to your shirt like a badge.

The cicada is a symbol of reincarnation.

Oh, Mum.

I'm sorry I asked Dad what x was worth.

I'm sorry I live in New South Wales.

I'm sorry I threw Cokie in the bin.

Maybe I should see a shrink?

12

Oh, come all ye faithful

Charter Towers, Raintree: September 2011

WELCOME TO EVENTIDE: PERSONAL SHOPPING: There is also a small shop located on the grounds where cigarettes, washing powder, confectionery and small gifts can be purchased.

Eventide Manual

I'm packing books for the move down to Raintree when I spy a little hardcover blue book in the bin. I fish it out. 'You didn't mean to throw this out, Dad?'

'It can go.' Dad looks above his glasses. 'Throw it in the bin.'

I open the little blue book, see the first page. 'You can't throw this out!'

'You want it, you keep it.' He gestures around the room. 'Take anything you want.'

I close the little blue book and slip it into my bag. 'Come on, Mum,' I say. 'We'll head down to Betty's shop now. I have to go and see a lady.'

Betty has the lease on the convenience store at Eventide. It used to be an attractive little shop until—after several break-ins—they covered it, wall to ceiling, in security screens. Betty's at her laptop. 'Careful when you open it; screen might fall out.' The laptop screen is held in place by strips of silver masking tape. 'Scooter stood on it.' Betty puts the kettle on. 'Just sit here, Mum.' Mum sits down like the good little girl that she is, that she always has been.

'I won't be long, Betty. Head's going to show me their room.'

'Tell her they want their double bed.'

At Raintree, Head takes me to a set of double doors: *Fred and Olive's Room* is painted on bright paper sprinkled with glitter. To the east, big plate-glass windows—windows are fixed, but the room's wonderfully light and airy, not dark like the clusters. I can already see my dad sitting at a much bigger desk, natural light spilling on his latest article. There's room for a coffee table and chairs over there. More space on the built-in dresser for Mum's makeup and toiletries.

'No double bed!' Head says. 'Regulations!'

I nod, nod, nod. *Yes, I understand.*

I understand that Regulation has no face and, even if it did, you don't dare try to smash it. 'It's really nice,' I say. 'I'll start bringing their stuff down tomorrow.'

'And we've got a little sing-song and morning tea at ten thirty,' Head says. 'Bring your mum and dad down, they'll enjoy it. Okay?'

'I'll do that,' I say. 'And thank you very much.'

I shut the door, sit down on a hospital bed and listen to the quietness.

Gardens are lovely, room is lovely, but the truth is, Raintree is a holding house for terminal humanity: poor lost souls who register neither protest nor understanding of the world around them; men and women who would otherwise be pissing, puking, drooling—offending everyday busy people going about their busyness. They're fed, washed, toileted, and for the remainder of the day they can *relax*: that is, hide from the bad men, sit and stare vacantly at the TV, lie praying on the lawn *Our Father who art in Heaven*, take a tumble into the garden beds, wander along the bars looking for a way home—or searching for missing wives or babies.

How long can an orderly dig out impacted colons, wipe diarrhoea from walls or change soiled linen before he asks, 'Why don't we let them die?' How many endless nights of bedsore bandages and night terrors before a nurse asks, 'Why can't we help them die?'

How long for my mum?

One year?

Ten?

I remember cutting glossy pictures of King Tut from one of my dad's *National Geographic*s and pasting them on paper card for school. Remember, too, learning that to make a mummy you stick a hook up a nostril and pull the brain out through the nose, piece by piece, and then you take the heart out of the chest cavity and put it in a bottle to keep it safe.

Mum's brain. Dad's heart.

I understand that I'm supposed to understand. I understand that Dad is rehearsing for the inevitable: in preparing for the day Mum leaves him, Dad is leaving Mum.

Each new day a repeat performance of yesterday's horrors …

> Vintery, mintery, cutery, corn,
> Apple seed and apple thorn,
> Wire, briar, limber lock
> Three geese in a flock
> One flew east
> One flew west
> And one flew over the cuckoo's nest.

At the end of *Cuckoo's Nest*, when Big Chief smothers McMurphy, you just *know* he has to do it; you *understand* he's got to do it, but you can't help wishing it had somehow all turned out different.

When Betty moved their double bed into the clusters, she had to sign a stat dec that she'd take care of the sheets. Sheets need washing every day now; there can be no more talk of double beds. *We can push those two hospital beds together and strap them ...*

I sit and listen to the silence. No sound of sobbing, just tears leaking down my face. Sometime in the next few days, I'm going to leave my mum in the care of these strangers; sometime in the coming week, I'm going to sit my mother on this bed: *Isn't this lovely, Mum? It's much nicer than your old room, isn't it, sweetheart?*

I wait in the reception area for someone to let me out.

'Murder!' Malka cries. 'God help me!'

*

Christmas Eve 2011

WELCOME TO RAINTREE: At Raintree, we have Recreation Officers who plan a variety of daily activities for your enjoyment. Existing interests can be pursued and new ones acquired. Outings and community activities are arranged on a regular basis and we make visitors and volunteers from the community welcome at any time.

Eventide Manual

You put your right hand in, you put your right hand out,
You put your right hand in, and you shake it all about.
You do the hokey-pokey and you turn yourself around.
That's what it's all about!

'I don't want to do this,' Mum says. 'Do I have to do this?'

'No, of course you don't, Mum. Let's sit this one out.'

The dining room is decked in Christmas finery. Aides are wheeling, leading, steering patients in from other wards. There are all manner of crutches, wheelchairs and wheelie beds, all manner of bandages, slack mouths and vacant eyes come to celebrate the festive season with us here at Raintree. Dad wouldn't come. We left Dad in *Fred and Olive's Room* listening to Gene Autry in his ear: 'You'll be sorry ...'

We left Dad weighing the pros and cons of going on a hunger strike. Pro: he'll get the media attention he wants. Con: will they find him mentally incompetent, lock him up and throw away the key? Because of Dad's letters to editors, Mental Health Queensland came to visit: *Are you going insane, Mr Bagnall?* Dad's had his own doubts recently. 'Come here,' he says to me. 'Listen to this.' I put my ear against my dad's big ear.

Big Ears: *Can't you hear that?*

Noddy: *No, Big Ears, I can't hear it; it's called auditory hallucination, Big Ears. I've read about it somewhere. Google it. Read this, Big Ears. See, people hear dogs barking, motorbikes revving, babies crying. You're not going insane, Big Ears.*

My dad's happy he's got music in his big ears and not dogs barking, motorbikes revving or babies crying. My dad says he can change the record anytime he wants just by humming a few bars: 'You'll be sorry ...'

Instead of listening to Gene Autry in his head, Dad could be here with Mum and me doing the hokey-pokey and listening to the Mingela Band. Mingela is a little one-goat, one-horse town half an hour from Charters Towers. Used to be four people in the Mingela Band—only old Mrs Wheatley on piano now.

Some oldies from other wards can still put their left leg in, and there are quite a few visitors putting their left leg in, their left leg out, but my mum doesn't want to put her left leg in. My darling little girl doesn't know her elbow from her arsehole.

If you're happy and you know it, clap your hands;
If you're happy and you know it, then you really ought to show it …

'Yes, please.' Spring rolls. White Christmas. Rumballs. 'Try this, Mum, it's soft.'

'Yes, please.' Cake and cream and cordial.

Wonder if you can stop pretending you're having fun when you're dead?

I don't know.

I know nothing. I'm quite at home in Raintree. Home is where the mother is.

Most days, not many visitors come to Raintree, but Daphne visits Ashley every day. Every day Daphne meets my eye, nods and smiles her understanding. Every day Daphne arrives in a tartan skirt and a pretty white lacy blouse. Every day Daphne takes her husband in to lunch and spoonfeeds her husband mush. Every day Daphne leaves with some dribble on her pretty lacy blouse, and every day S-bend Ashley wanders around looking into faces. 'Daphne?' he asks hopefully. 'Are you Daphne?'

No one visits Paulie. 'Hello, dear!' Paulie says. 'Did you see my baby?' Every day Paulie shows me her baby. 'You have a beautiful baby, Paulie.' Paulie wears a footballer's padded headgear because Paulie took a tumble in the broom closet looking for her baby. Today, for the festive season, Paulie's football headgear is decked with reindeer antlers.

I'm-Scott-Dagleish-from-Riverview sits in the corner in pyjama bottoms and slippers. I'm-Scott-Dagleish-from-Riverview is the man once strong enough to spider his way, arms and legs extended, down a well to save his son lying blacked out at the bottom.

Every day I'm-Scott-Dagleish-from-Riverview sits in the corner in pyjama bottoms and slippers.

'Yes, please.' Apricot kisses and angel wings. 'Try these, Mum. These are soft.'

My mum doesn't have her teeth in; the cleaning lady stole them.

Mingela Band plays 'What a friend we have in Jesus' and we all sing along. Mingela Band plays 'Rudolph the red-nosed reindeer' and I remember how every Christmas my mum had a glass of bubbly for the toasts, and if my mum had two glasses of bubbly her nose went red and she got the giggles. How, when Dad made a speech, Mum put her arms around his neck and told again how Dad *came walking down the road with Peggy the pig in a sling*, and how she thought, *He's the one for me*. And my dad would say, *You've got a red nose, woman—you're tipsy!*

Mingela Band plays 'Jingle bells' and we all sing along.

Party is nearly over; aides are clearing tables when Josie ushers a little white-haired hobgoblin up the front. 'Listen, everybody.' Josie holds up a hand for quiet. 'This is Tilly.'

In pretty pastel floral, little Tilly is nervous and excited. Tilly has a wonderful head of snow-white hair. The bun on Tilly's head is tied with tinsel. You can see the bun on top of Tilly's head because God's made a question mark out of Tilly; Tilly is so badly humped her little face can only face the floor.

'Tilly is from Mingela,' Josie says, 'and she would like to recite a poem for you.'

Wheelie beds are being queued at the door when Tilly from Mingela states roundly: '"Lost"! A poem by A.B. "Banjo" Paterson.'

Tilly's away!

'He ought to be home,' said the old man, 'without there's
    something amiss.
'He only went to the Two-mile—he ought to be back by this.

'He *would* ride the Reckless filly, he *would* have his wilful way;
'And, here, he's not back at sundown—and what will his
     mother say?'

Little humped shoulders swaying to the rhythm, Tilly's hands
play out the drama:

'He was always his mother's idol, since ever his father died;
'And there isn't a horse on the station that he isn't game to ride.
'But that Reckless mare is vicious, and if once she gets away—'

'Yarrrhhhh!' Bobby comes to inspect Tilly from Mingela.
'Yarrrhhhh!'
Take Bobby away! Can't someone please come and take him away!
Teddy under arm: 'Yarrrhhhh!' Bobby pulls his lip up to his nose.
'Yarrrrrhhhhhhh!'
Little Tilly doesn't falter. Tilly's little slippered feet are playing
out the drama:

The old man walked to the sliprail, and peered up the dark'ning
track—

'Yarrrrrhhhhhh!'
An old boy stands up and tells Bobby, 'Shuddup! Shuddup!
Shuddup!'
Tilly soldiers on:

'What has become of my Willie?—why isn't he home to-night?'

Someone leads Bobby *yarrh-yarrhing* away. Oldies nearest the
door take it as a cue, and begin shuffling out.
Don't go! Can't you see? This is Tilly from Mingela performing!

For the Reckless mare had smashed him against a leaning limb,
And his comely face was battered, and his merry eyes were dim.

Mum stands up. 'Can we go now, love?'
'Just one more minute, Mum. I'm watching Tilly from Mingela.'
'I've got to be going now,' Mum says.

And the mother kept feebly calling, with a hope that would not die,
'Willie! where are you, Willie?' But how can the dead reply …

Chairs scrape on lino.
Tilly soldiers on:

'God pity the stricken mother, and answer the widow's prayer!'

Mum says, 'Can we go now, love?'
I hold her hand. 'Okay, Mum, just give me one more minute.'

'I know that sooner or later I shall find my boy,' she said.
But she came not home one evening, and they found her lying
    dead,
And stamped on the poor pale features, as the spirit homeward
    pass'd,
Was an angel smile of gladness—she had found the boy at last.

I give Tilly from Mingela a standing ovation—*if you're happy and
you know it, then you really ought to show it*—but the dining room is
nearly empty now.

'Come on, sweetheart,' I say to Mum. 'Come this way so I can
say hello to Tilly … Tilly?' I touch her shoulder and bend down so
Tilly from Mingela can see my face. 'That was wonderful!' I tell her.
'Truly wonderful!'

Tilly, flushed and excited, tilts her head to see me.

There's a sparkle in Tilly's eye, a smile on her lips. 'Blast!' Tilly scolds, punching a fist into her palm. 'I left out two lines!' Her faded blue eyes flash up at me: 'Do you think anyone noticed?'

'No, Tilly, I don't think anyone noticed.'

I put my arm around Mum. 'Come on, Mum, we can go now.' Mum doesn't have her little black walking cane; the cleaning lady stole it.

Mum's in a hurry. 'Gotta get to the toilet.'

'This way, sweetheart.'

I pull down the padded panties.

Mum holds the bar and lowers herself onto the seat.

I nuzzle her cheek, and tease, 'Who's got a poopy bum?'

She leans away, trying to see me. 'What did you say?'

I lean in and whisper, 'Who's got a poopy bum?'

Mum pulls away, raises a crooked finger. 'If you ever say something like that again,' she says fiercely, 'you'll never be invited into this house again!'

'I'm sorry, Mum—'

'Never again!' She pushes my hands away, tries to stand by herself.

I'm sorry ... I pull a handful of wet wipes ... *so sorry ...* clean her as best I can.

Her hand in mine, my arm about her waist, I lead her into *Fred and Olive's Room.*

'I'm sorry, Mum.' I help her onto the bed. 'I'm truly sorry.'

Mum turns her head on the pillow, toothless mouth an unforgiving line.

'What happened?' Dad looks up from writing.

'Nothing, Dad.' My voice catches. 'I just said something really stupid.

'I'm sorry, Mum.' I touch her cheek. 'You know I wouldn't hurt you for the world?'

Mum stares at the ceiling: shame, too deep for words, dampening her pillow.

i ... am so small ... so empty ... i might just ... disappear.

*

New Year 2012

I love old people. I didn't always love old people: old people were shrinking pools of shade you sidestepped on the footpath; old people cluttered up the highways with their vans and trailers; old people held up supermarket queues digging in their purses for change. *Hurry up, Mum! You're holding up the queue!* I love old people now. I don't mind waiting while some old girl tells the pharmacist how she slept last night and how *he* slept last night—*You know what he's like.* Inside every shrinking pool of light is a little girl or boy who dared to dream.

Aussie Outback Oasis Van Park is home when you haven't got a home to go to. What used to be a Chinee-apple and spear-grass paddock is landscaped bushland now: oasis for grey nomads with nothing better to do than clutter up the highways with their vans and trailers. Big highway sign says 'George Ellis Drive', named after good ol' Doc Ellis who put nine stitches in my head and fished a tooth out of my throat. It'd be good leaving your name somewhere other than a four-inch plaque on a wall.

Charters Towers Pony Club Ground is just up there along the highway. I like going past and seeing what jumps are up, and how high they're set. I miss it. Miss my little chestnut mare, Natasha. Six bar was her specialty—could jump higher than herself with a beanpole swaying on her back. Mum bought me and my horses a little paddock over there, and I'm remembering how, one time when Natasha had an injured knee, Mum drove out to heat-pack it every night at ten thirty for weeks—after working all day at the

207

cafe—while I was asleep in bed; and how Greg shot Natasha for me when all her teeth fell out.

Walk the whole block and come back past All Souls St Gabriels.

Red-brick double-storey dining room is an impressive building. It has an honours board that covers the back wall. Names of Head Boy one side and Dux of the Year the other side ever since the year dot. I was odds-on favourite; lesbian bikie's moll tapping her cane against her leg said, 'Now you study hard,' (study?) 'we're all counting on you!' Counting on me to be the first female in the history of the world to get her name up on the all-boys honours board. I didn't get it. Dracula got it. Drac—a new boy, came in Grade Eleven—was as skinny as me and half a head taller and tried to hide it with a stoop. Big set of buck teeth dubbed him 'Dracula' the day he arrived at All Souls. I don't think he minded; everyone called him Drac. Besides, by Grades Eleven and Twelve, you were allowed to get good marks. Last I heard, Drac was a vet somewhere in Ireland—or was it Wales? Me? I'm still waiting for Godot. Still learning how to live, and got to start learning how to die. Didn't give a rat's patootie at the time about not getting dux: couldn't wait to get out into the *real* world and start my *real* life. Now I'm thinking it'd be good to leave your name somewhere other than a four-inch plaque on a wall. Never told Mum and Dad I nearly got dux—even at the Olympic Games no one really gives a rat's arse about who won silver and bronze.

There's an email doing the circuit of the internet: *The trouble with school reunions is that all your mates are so old and wrinkled, they can't recognise you anymore. Ha! Ha!*

End of Grade Twelve, they matched everyone with a song. I got 'Bony Moronie'. What happened to that slim young body I so despised?

Walk for an hour but I still haven't lost even one of the twelve kilos I've put on in the last twelve months, so I go down to the supermarket and get a supersize packet of potato chips (rock salt, 50 per cent less fat). I don't mind old people on gophers in supermarket aisles—only fat people shouldn't be cluttering up the aisles on their gophers. Media and taxman come after smokers; why don't they go after fat people? If McDonald's cost twenty dollars a packet, maybe there wouldn't be so many fat people cluttering up supermarkets with their gophers. THOU SHALT NOT PERSECUTE MINORITIES—EXCEPT SMOKERS! And what about all these cars polluting the atmosphere? If petrol cost twenty dollars a packet, maybe the whole goddamned world wouldn't be falling apart!

World fell apart when Granny Chapman died. Who'd have thought? I like to think that if only Granny's four daughters had been involved, it wouldn't have fallen apart, but throw in sons-in-law and solicitors …

Never mind.

Suffice it to say, death duties—followed by a drastic slump in cattle and property prices—and three years of solicitors took the bulk of Granny Chapman's estate. Not long after, my Aunty June died of cancer. Aunty June was forty-nine, and her Irish eyes weren't smiling. Aunty Melva eventually sent Uncle Owen—and his big smile—packing. *Well, ya can't help bad luck, can ya?* Uncle Ian and his twitchy eyebrows had some more troubles and shot through—some say maybe Darwin. My Aunty Dulcie spends Christmas with us now.

We'll celebrate the New Year 2012 here at Aussie Outback Oasis. Greg's driving up. He'll head Mum off at the pass when she tries to escape down the stairs—*Gotta be going home now*—and I'll serve up Red Rooster, potato salad and coleslaw. I'll thump my dad's back when he chokes on a piece of chicken, and I'll serve up four ice-creams on sticks. Standing at the sink, I'll watch my mum—*Let me help, love*—drying dishes. She'll take the plate in tiny, knobbly hands, wipe, turn and wipe. I'll watch the dribble of concentration creep down her chin, elongate, fall: wipe, turn and wipe. I never cried when Granny Chapman died—dying is what mean old grannies do—and I never really understood Mum's anguish, when Granny died. I do now. Understand, too, why 'the heart' is seen as the 'seat of love', because that's where it hurts the most.

I guess, as a family, we were never adequately inoculated against loss and grief. Until Robyn died. My dad's mum and dad, and all of his brothers and sisters, lived until well into their eighties. My Uncle Bert smoked all his life and died of lung cancer when he was eighty-eight. Robyn—never smoked a cigarette in her life—died of lung cancer at fifty-four.

Go figure.

Except ... a memory long since forgotten resurfaces: a story about how Granny Chapman caught Robyn and Jennifer smoking, when they were fourteen, up behind the cowshed. Granny sat them down at the kitchen table, and told them they had to smoke the whole packet. They didn't get that far: they both threw up before they did.

Wish Granny Chapman had caught me smoking when I was fourteen ...

Sitting on the veranda of a cabin at Aussie Outback Oasis, I take from my bag the little blue book I fished out of Dad's bin. It's a small, hardcover notebook, with three little strips of red tape you punch letters into. Top left-hand corner: *Olive*. Top right-hand corner: *Fred*. A little lower, between *Olive* and *Fred*: *Our Journey*.

First page:

Olive May Chapman
and
Frederick Francis Bagnall
Married at St. Gabriel's Chapel
on
October, First, 1947.

Second page: *Honeymoon, 3rd October: Came to Mackay in train ...*

I flip to the back. Second-last entry: *2008, October 1st, 61st Anniversary.*

I turn the page: 2009—blank, and the next. *Blank. Blank. Blank.*

In this little book, my dad's recorded every trip they did together—several every year—until 2009. And I wonder about the optimism of a man, the supreme faith of a man, on his wedding day beginning a journal entitled *Olive – Fred: Our Journey.*

I wonder too about the misery of a man, the utter desolation of a man, who would throw that precious little book in the bin.

I burned all my diaries when Mum and Dad packed up and left the anabranch. Read years later that you should never burn your diaries: it's a symbolic act of self-immolation.

*

17/01/12
Dear Sir/Madam

Editors can suppress unpalatable truths; distasteful topics can be shelved and disturbing facts kept dark, but the intellectual cowardice of the naysayers is not the only challenge facing advocates of euthanasia.

I am pro-euthanasia. The only thing I find 'distasteful' or 'disturbing' in the debate is that the inevitable legalisation of 'the right to die' will be motivated by economics, not compassion.

A recent Queensland current affairs program aired a segment on the 'buy-now-pay-later' mentality of Generation X; a second (supposedly unrelated) piece dealt with the ageing population—concluding there will soon be 75,000 people suffering from dementia.

Blind Freddy can see these two horsemen are on course for collision: a generation crippled by debt, responsible for the care (cost) of ever-increasing numbers of aged cripples?

Mark my words: in the not-too-distant future, politicians will be scrambling for a seat on the Euthanasia Band Wagon; the genuine cries of Catholic protest will be silenced by the rabble, and the noble 'Let them die with dignity!' will be nothing but a euphemism for: 'Time to bump the old boys off!'

There's an unpalatable *truth* for you. Let your false teeth chew on that!

Faithfully,
Daughter of Blind Freddy

No one published it, Dad. Not one damned paper.

13

Through a glass darkly

It's not the caring for that gets you;
it's the simultaneous grieving for, undoes you.

Charters Towers, Raintree: June 2012

Don't think about it; don't dwell on it.

You sidestep it, but it's always there: one step behind you, one step in front of you, it's always there ... in the corner of your eye ... whispering in your ear ...

I saw it this morning.

In dressing-gown and retro-red stilettos, Death came dancing down a corridor, twirling a black cane, and trying to master a tricky new routine: *One step forward, two steps back, double tap, sashay, twirl, twirl, twirl.*

'Oh, Death!'

You called? Death stops mid-step, eyes surprised. *Ah, it's you, Judas!*

'You're late!'

Critics! Death sniffs. *'You're all the same: too late! Too early! I'm an Artist!* He doffs his beret, spreads his arms. *Raintree: work in progress, 'Death-in-Life'. Or do you prefer 'Life-in-Death'?*

In the furthest corner of the garden, my mum is feeling her way along the fence.

Ashley, in pyjama bottoms, is lying on the lawn: 'Our Father, who art in Heaven …'

'That's my mother's walking stick you've got. Can I have it?'

My dream! My rules! Death twirls the stick. *Finders keepers!*

'And Ashley's dressing-gown!'

Peek-a-boo! Death admires the dangly bits peeking from the leg of padded panties. *I'm offended you're offended,* he says stiffly. *Hardly pornographic!*

'Hardly decent!'

I don't do decent. Death clicks his heels, lands lightly on Ashley's back. *But nothing wrong with a little grotesquery!* He tightropes along Ashley's spine, stiletto heels printing bedsores in his back. *It's the grotesque keeps me going.* Death springs down and confides, *They're all late, you know! Just the paperwork to do!*

I made a joke! Did you get it? Death eyes me closely. *Oh, never mind!* he mutters, stalking me across the lawn. *You never did have a sense of humour. All egoists are serious people; all serious people are—*

'You should keep your paperwork up to date.'

Death shrugs, spreads his hands. *Just letting nature take its own corpse, as it were. Another joke! And yet, you're not laughing!* He hurries after me. *Sorry. Been a long time since anyone around here demanded anything beyond slapstick grotesque.* Catching up, Death twirls the stick. *I love a good joke,* he confesses. *A good joke is poison to the ego.*

'And yet …' I look into his face—a face without guile. 'You're not laughing?'

All my laughter I must do alone, Death tells me. *He who tells the joke has to be very serious; he cannot laugh with you.*

'Hello, dear.' Paulie smiles, folding back her shawl. 'Did you see my baby?'

And what a cute little baby it is! Death pulls the doll from Paulie's arms, tosses it cartwheeling into the blue. *Wheeeeee!* He tracks its flight. *Ke-thunk!*

'Slapstick!'

It's my job! Death twirls the walking stick into a black umbrella. *It's what I do!*

'You're a thief. You've stolen everything!'

Dolls, umbrellas, slippers? Death shrugs. *Petty larceny!*

On hands and knees, I push between the yellow bars and border shrubs.

Treasure hunt! Death slinks along the fence with me. *Love a good treasure hunt. Whole thing is foolishness, of course: the hide-and-seeker, the hide-and-seeking—the sought.*

'I was talking about choice, privacy, purpose.'

So was I! Death sits on my heels. *Petty larceny.*

'Here's your baby, Paulie. There you go, don't cry now.'

Death plucks the doll from Paulie's arms again, tosses it cartwheeling into the blue. *Ke-thunk!*

'You win.'

That's a given! Death passes through the bars.

'Don't go! You can't leave them like this!'

Tomorrow is as good a day to die as any other.

'But you've already plucked their wings!'

And now I'm off to catch some more, before they fly away.

'Death! Before you go! My mum's teeth ... I've looked everywhere. Please.'

If you insist.

'Thank you!' I rummage in the leaf litter. 'Thank you!'

Death's heading for the highway singing, *So long, farewell* ...

Mum comes, feeling her way along the bars. Her hand touches mine. 'Hello?'

'It's me, Mum.' I kiss her hand. 'I found your teeth, see? Come inside, sweetheart, we'll give them a wash, and you can tell me what you've been doing.'

'Oh, you know,' Mum says. 'Just lookin' after the horses, love.'

Death is nothing—a black umbrella twirling in the distance. But I can still hear his song.

*

June 2012

ANTICIPATORY GRIEF: also called the long goodbye and living death.

SYMPTOMS: more sadness—and more guilt.

Betty's going on holiday before Betty *goes insane.*

'Get some mangoes for Dad,' Betty says, pulling up at the corner store. 'An' get me one of them big snakes too.'

Root around on the floor of Betty's car and you'll find enough coin for half a dozen mangoes, one big jelly snake and a supersize packet of chips (rock salt, 50 per cent less fat).

Betty and Bill are going to Europe—to meet up with their two girls in Paris—before Betty *goes insane.* Dad calls Betty's place 'the menagerie', when Betty isn't listening, and I'm going to housesit the menagerie so Betty can go to Europe for a month before Betty *goes insane.*

I'm going to swim every morning before I go to Raintree. In a pretty blue swimsuit patterned by darker flowers (mother by proxy) lap after lap after lap ... *my mother doesn't know me anymore* ... lap after lap after lap … *this can't be happening* … lap after lap … *not to our family* … lap after lap … *not to my mum.*

In or out of the pool is like seeing and hearing the world through water.

Over my head. Out of my depth. Lap after lap.

On the way to Betty's we pass the showgrounds: ferris wheel, Joy-Whizzer, carnies, stalls and tents. Hot chips, hot dogs and Mr Whippy. Goosenecks, triple decks and fully decked-out motor-homes. Far cry from pony-club kids selling tickets to hire Barry Renton's cattle truck.

Last time I rode at the Charters Towers Show, I had three broken toes—Blue had jumped on my foot a month before. Last time I rode at the Charters Towers Show Mum cracked my tailbone in two places.

You can still hear the loudspeakers echoing, *Testing, one-two-three*, as we bounce across the grid onto Betty's place and Scooter races us down the dusty road.

'Don't know what's wrong with him,' Betty says as we pull in beside the house. 'He's been goin' apeshit all day.'

Betty doesn't know what's got Scooter going apeshit. I do: Scooter's a retired racehorse; it's the sound of loudspeakers that has Scooter's tail up.

Betty's parked with house fence front and side, and paddock fence the other side.

'You shouldn't park here,' I tell Betty, as Scooter veers away and laps the paddock. 'He could get himself jammed up in here, carry-ing on like that.'

'Always park here,' Betty says, getting out. 'Bring Dad's mangoes,' Betty says, lumping plastic bags of canned dog and cat food from the boot.

Hello! Hello! A big Dalmatian-cross-pig-dog bounds through the gate. *What you got in them bags?* Boofhead asks. *Anything for me?*

'Get your nose outta there, Boofhead!'

'Duck food's on the back veranda,' Betty says. 'And change their water every day.' Cage of white rats on the back veranda. 'Used to be six, one got away.' Wombles, a fat black cat, sometimes throws epileptic fits when he hears his food dish rattled. 'Don't worry if he chucks a wobbly,' Betty says. 'He'll just look dead for a bit, but usually comes right out of it.' Chooks and bantams roost in four dead cars in long grass down the back. 'Bill's gonna do 'em up, when he gets around to it. And oughta check the back of Bill's ute, too: chooks sometimes lay in that.' Billie's two Shetlands, Kahlua and Tequila: Tequila won Led Shetland High Jump last year at the show.

And there's George. Poor little flea-bitten George has seen better days. 'Hello, Georgie!' Little Shetland Mum bought thirty years ago to teach the grandkids how to ride.

'Come on,' Betty says. 'I'll show you the best roads to walk Boofy.' Boofhead races out in front, carrying her lead. 'Get back here, Boofy! Not many dogs on this road,' Betty says. 'But you might wanna take a stick.'

Stirred up by the echoes of the loudspeaker, Scooter's racing Shetlands up the road. Tail up, Scooter's reliving his younger days—heydays—on the track.

And, suddenly, so am I.

*

Charters Towers Show: 1978

Mum has a pot of hoof black in one hand, paintbrush in the other.

'You've missed a bit, Mum—on the inside hind.'

Mum squats down to touch up Blue's hooves. Can't do it myself: I'm wearing white jodhpurs. Snow-white jodhpurs. *Don't know how you expect me to get this saddle grease out!* Mum's had my jodhpurs soaking in a bucket of Snow White overnight. I look good: that's boobs I got in my bra, not cotton wool; no knickers—you can't get a *smooth line* wearing knickers under skin-tight, snow-white jodhpurs; black riding jacket Mum made on her new Singer; black rubber knee-length riding boots that *could* be leather from a distance. *Hair by Stefan?* I look good, and the whole world's got nothing better to do than be watching me and thinking, *Doesn't she look good!*

Blue dances sideways. 'Mum! Stand on the other side!'

Blue has black boot polish on his points and eyes. His big ears are clipped and blackened too. Blue has magic silver white in his tail; his tail is *silky silver, with subtle hues of violet.* For an ugly big mongrel, Blue (Oliver, for official purposes today) looks pretty good too.

'Hello, matey.' Greg offers Blue a bit of hot dog. 'How's he going?'

Blue cocks his nose at hot dog. Blue's lipping Greg's stubbie: *Rather have a sip of XXXX, mate.*

Greg's just arrived home from three weeks on a boat—first cattle boatload of live export to Hong Kong. Greg's here to ride Blue home when I finish my last event. I'm nursing (milking) broken toes for all they're worth. Greg wants to buy Blue, now I'm going to Europe, but Robyn won't let him so I'm going to lease him to Ricky Grubb.

While Greg and Blue share a XXXX and skite about how they won Best Pick-up Team at the Ravenswood and Charters Towers rodeos, I'm watching the course builders put another row of hay bales on the Ace. Ace stands at six foot two. *Blue's never jumped under lights ... and it's starting to drizzle ... gonna be slippery.*

Eric Ormond spruiks, 'And this is a local rider competing in the Pack of Cards.' Then Eric Ormond spruiks, 'And that was a clear round to Oliver, on fifty-four points.'

'Matey!' Greg says, holding Blue at the bit. 'That was fantastic!'

I dismount. 'Help me get this boot off, would ya?'

Mum says, 'Won't you be in the jump-off, love?'

'Score's not high enough.' I toss my skullcap at Mum. *Hair by Stefan?* 'I only took the ten, Jack and Queen. The professional riders will take the big cards: Ace and King.'

Pack of Cards was my last event; show's all over for me, my dream of competing at the Olympic Games long since relegated to childhood fantasy. But it's the first time Blue's competed in the Open and I'm happy—damp and happy: wet jodhpurs cling like skin.

Blue cocks his nose at me. *What's that smell?*

Mum cocks her nose at me. 'What's that smell?'

I don't know, but it's wafting all around me, and it smells like … bleach.

Mum turns me. 'Oh dear!' she says, covering a smile with her hand.

'What is it?' I twist around, trying to see my backside. And then I can see my backside: snow-white jodhpurs are split from crotch to waist. *No knickers!*

Damp has reactivated the bleach. 'You had the bleach too strong!'

Mum's trying not to laugh. 'Here, let me see.' Mum pulls the two sides together. 'I'll probably be able to mend them.' Mum tugs, and the front seam splits from crotch to waist.

'It's not funny!' *You had 'em in bleach too long!*

'I know.' Mum jams a hand between her legs. 'I know.' Mum has her knees jammed together. 'I know it's not funny, love—'

'It's not funny!' *Not funny when it's your bum hanging out!* 'Shut up, Mum!' *And the whole world's watching.* I slap her arm. 'Stop it!'

Mum can't stop it. 'Oh, get over yourself!' Mum slaps my slapping hand.

Blue steps back on my foot; I knee-jerk his belly before he can put his weight down.

All Mum sees is me kicking my horse, in what she thinks is bad temper.

Toe of Mum's boot, square on my tailbone, drops me like a rock. God, I miss it.

*

June 2012

It's dusk when Betty and I get back from walking Boofhead. You can see the glow of the showground lights over there; night air echoes with showground excitement.

I leased Blue to Ricky Grubb to take on the show circuit—*I'm off to Europe*—but I heard that Blue tossed Ricky headfirst into the first jump in the first event at the Charters Towers Show the following year. Ricky left in an ambulance with a badly broken leg. Greg brought Blue back to the anabranch. Greg was happy, so was Blue.

Ricky? Not so much.

We've left the side gate open. Front screen door is open too. *I'm sure I shut it?*

I'm thinking break-in, but Betty grumbles, 'That damned George!'

Betty heads across the veranda, steps on a plate of dog food: tin plate shoots out from under her, clatters across cement; a fat black cat chucking a wobbly hurtles between her legs. Astonished, Boofhead sees Betty land on hands and knees. *You wanna play?* Boofhead jumps on Betty: *See if I can lick your ears!*

Betty cups her ears and squeals.

Just like a pig! Boofy straddles Betty's head. *Left ear! Right ear! Left ...*

Betty's glasses break at the silver tape. I catch her by the ears— Boofy not Betty—and yank her off. *That was fun!* Boofy chases her tail in circles. *That was fun!*

Betty takes my hand, brushes her skinned knees. 'I've had just about enough of you lot!' Betty threatens. 'Get out the back, Boofhead!'

Boofhead jumps the front fence, chases Scooter chasing Shetlands across the flat. Grinning, Boofhead looks back at Scooter: *Wanna race?*

You bet! Scooter cranks his tail up a notch. *Shetlands are no fun.*

Boofhead jams her tail, pins back her ears.

Racing! Tequila missed the start, Boofhead got away clean, Kailua forced into the rail, down the back straight Scooter goes wide round Chrysler, settles. Boofhead runs down Rhode Island Red, Speckled Sussex leaves the track ... I think there'll be a protest ... they come into the home straight, Scooter three lengths in front, Boofhead on Scooter ... they're neck and neck ... but it's Scooter—Scooter wheels into the Winner's Circle, between car and fence—Scooter wins the Menagerie Millions!

Jammed up, Scooter rears. Boofhead swinging from his tail, Scooter's hooves crash down on the car bonnet. Snorting, Scooter spins, kicks up, double-barrels the grille, smashing two headlights and a spottie.

I look at Betty. Betty looks at me.

Betty shrugs. 'Bill can fix it.'

You dead or what? Boofhead nudges Wombles. *You missed all the fun!*

'And you wonder why I'm going insane?' Betty nudges the paralytic cat with a broken sandal. 'Get up, you!' Betty tells Wombles. 'Get up! Or I'll have you put down.'

Boofhead has baulked at the open front door. Tail wagging, Boofhead looks back and barks: *Would'ja get a look at this!*

George is in the lounge. The little Shetland has five mango seeds between his hooves. He spits out the last seed, wipes his muzzle on the sofa: *Any more?*

'Get outta there, George!' Betty rants. 'Or I'll have you put down too!'

Really! George raises his tail, poops on the carpet.

If Mum were here, she'd pee herself.

If Mum were here, she'd ...

Oh, Mum!

When caring for a dementia patient there will be some moments of recognition and clarity, and glimpses of clarity and love. Cherish them. But most of the time ... well ... then there's most of the time.

In silence, we watch through the windows that fill *Fred and Olive's Room* with light.

Outside, my mum—*tap, tap, step*—is feeling her way along the window ledge, *tap, tap, step.*

My mum, her face seriously bruised again. 'I saw it happen,' Dad says. 'She was coming across the lawn, put her foot in a hole, went face first into that brick wall.'

When Mum's opposite, Dad raps the glass, frustration sounding in his knuckles. Mum doesn't falter: *tap, tap, step*; *tap, tap, step*. She can't hear him; she can't see him—glass is tinted, and Mum almost blind.

Ashley, too, is tap-tapping his way along the ledge. Mum's hand touches Ashley's. Startled, Mum withdraws her hand, then she hears Ashley crying. We watch Mum put her arms around Ashley; we watch Ashley pull back, surprised: 'Daphne?'

We watch Mum rest her cheek against Ashley's chest, and murmur as she pats him. Mum is still attuned to the social signals that indicate another's distress.

Dad's at his desk, in pyjamas and jumper. I'm standing beside him wearing his dressing-gown over my clothes. *It's freezing in here.*

No, we can't turn the air-con down—a man has to come up from Townsville to adjust the setting.

'Your mother's gone,' Dad says, throwing down his pen. 'She's not coming back.'

I glance at Dad. We are watching the same scene through pretty much the same eyes, but my dad just doesn't get it—can't get it? won't get it?

Wonder if a piece of four-by-two wrapped around his big ears would help him get it?

Dad's trying to write an article for the *Northern Miner*: 'Parks of Charters Towers', but scattered on the desk are multiple distractions. *ABC News: Survey shows support for legalised euthanasia. Taboo Subject: Silence as People Suffer. Condemned to a life in limbo, ready to die: I am ninety-five years old, watching my wife of sixty-four years dying slowly.*

I put a hand on his shoulder, feel his despair—frustration so palpable it's a physical ache. 'I've never been so glad to see anyone in all my life,' my dad said when I came home this time. *Thank you for approving of me, Dad; I'll hold your hand when you die.* We play chess; I cut his hair and toenails; I take him up town—*places to go, people to see.*

When Mum's not falling in holes and smashing her face into brick walls, she's gazing into the mirror, inviting herself to come inside. 'Fred, there's someone at the front door, but they won't come inside.' When my mum's not inviting herself to come inside, she's tracking the fence looking for the horses; when not tracking the fence line, she's sitting in the far corner of the gardens with her feet stuck through the bars, staring up at crucifixes transfixed against blue sky. 'This foot back first, Mum. Now this one. Now let's get these ants off you, sweetheart.'

We watch as Mum slips her arm through Ashley's arm. We watch as they totter across the lawn; we watch until they reach the garden at the yellow fence where Ashley picks a flower; Mum takes it, pats his hand.

I'm glad my mum is Daphne, even for a little while.

Mum's cognitive function is all but gone, but we've just seen proof that she can still read emotion. The favoured mode of the rational mind is words; but 90 per cent of an emotional message is nonverbal. Are such messages—frustration in his voice, frustration in a gesture—being absorbed unconsciously? Might not some parallel stream of consciousness be aware of what is happening, and not be lost in it? Is her soul—wraith-like observer—watching her demented double?

'Dad,' I try again. 'Dad, please don't talk in front of Mum like she's not there. It would break her heart if for one second she thought you didn't love her anymore.'

'Your mother's gone.' Dad dismisses my argument. 'She's not coming back.'

This *is* Mum. *This* is part of her life's journey.

Your mother's gone—dashing it with insensitivity because he hasn't an inkling that such notions exist, or should exist. *She's not coming back.* Coping mechanism: dispassionate reasoning impervious to reason—men don't understand that women seek shelter in emotional connectedness.

Have you ever seen him hold her? Hug her? Ever?

No, not in public, but ...

No time ago, I was hugging my mum, nuzzling her neck, making her giggle.

'I wish your father would do that,' Mum said. 'He used to, you know?'

'Dad. Dad! Did you hear what Mum just said?'

Dad's half deaf. Mum's half blind.

Concentrate on an idea for too long, like a moth, you begin to go in circles: Mum is centre and circumference. *Your mother's gone*:

confirmation of how things are and how they always would be. *She's not coming back.* He is who he is—who he had always been—and his qualities are ones Mum loved and depended on all her life. If the value she placed on them—or her needs—had changed, that had to be her fault.

But the tears making me blink are caused by something deeper than his apparent lack of empathy. That ABC radio interview Dad did last year? I didn't tell you at the time, I was too ashamed of him—shamed for him—but when I brought Mum into the room, Dad looked up, saw us, finished his interview with Nathalie Fernbach from the ABC: '… can't go to any of these entertainments; she just goes and stares into space … she doesn't hear anything … or anything.'

Mum did hear him. And she understood.

I take my hand from his shoulder. I shrug out of his dressing-gown.

Where are you going? Downtown to buy a piece of four-by-two.

'This could go on for ten years!' Dad says. 'She's ten years younger than me.'

'I know, Dad.'

You are hereby condemned to remain at Raintree for the term of your natural life.

Hippocratic oath imposes two duties—prolong life, relieve suffering—but protracted emotional suffering is torture too; emotional pain can't be seen, bandaged, sutured, and watching a loved one suffer erodes belief in the sanctity of life.

Euthanasia on request will come; and I am shuddered by the thought that it will be seen as so cost effective that it will be encouraged. Tax rebates for euthanasia volunteers? Bonuses for doctors for euthanasia procedures? Euthanasia franchises?

It will come, but not in Dad's time. Dad has his tablets. I helped him hide his stash in that photo frame over there. It's not just about his right to take his own life; it's more about his knowing that he has an option: psychological relief in having some control. But the unpredictability of taking sleeping tablets is a sticking point—not like he can hold a plastic bag over his own head. I've rung people for my dad, taken advice from secretive voices, anonymous faces: *eating a full bowl of custard first might help.* Betty's gone online and ordered a book from America. I've emailed every current affairs program in Australia in an attempt to keep him going. *Sorry, we don't have anything scheduled on euthanasia. We'll let you know.*

Back in January, a young bloke came up from Townsville and interviewed my dad—a five-minute segment at the tail end of WIN News.

And not one phone call about it! Not one damned phone call!

Among the scattered papers on the desk is the latest report from Queensland Health.

Dear Mr Frederick Bagnall

... you were assessmed [sic] by two mental health clinicians ... you consented to our assessment hoping it might help your attempts to advocate for law reform concerning euthanasia ... you clearly stated you would not end your life, if your wife could not also at the same time. Collateral from nursing staff at Eventide reported no changes in your sleep, appetite or motivation, which would be expected if you where [sic] depressed and suicidal.

Your mental risk domains (suicide, aggression, vulnerability and disengagement) have been rated low ... you displayed no signs or symptoms of altered mood, speech or thought disorder. It was ... my impression that you are not suffering a depression or psychotic illness. Furthermore, that you are not a risk to yourself and your wife ...

It was a pleasure to meet you Fred.

I've read that anyone has the potential to be a killer—it's just the circumstance that's different. The thought of being watched by a murderer skulking in the shadows is chilling; far more chilling to watch your father in pyjamas watch your mother through a window.

Dad's not terminally ill, but he is terminally old.

Trading desperation for distraction, I write to the City Council. Reply:

CHARTERS TOWERS REGIONAL COUNCIL
(Exceptional Service for an Exceptional Community)

10 July 2012
Dear Pamela
Re: Naming of small park near Venus Battery

Reference is made to your letter received by Council on 14 June 2012 regarding your request to have the small park near the Venus Battery named in honour of your father, Mr Fred Bagnall.

Council is pleased to advise that at its meeting held 20 June 2012 a resolution to agree to this request was passed. Further communication pertaining to a ceremony and a suitable date will be forthcoming in the near future.

*

Thou shalt not put to death that which is not already dying.

Charters Towers, Raintree: 1 August 2012

'I'll come back up for the ceremony, Dad, but they said it could be a month or two; the *Fred Bagnall Park* sign has to come from Melbourne.'

Dad's at his desk. 'It's freezing in here.'

Morgue temp, Death explains. *Don't want rotting corpses cluttering up the place.*

I'm snuggled under the doona, hand in hand, face to face, with my mum.

Poor little baby bird, poor little bruised face: eyes, little crescent moons, staring at eternity. How long before I'm saying, *In the end, you see, it was a blessing?*

It was Mum's birthday yesterday. She turned eighty-five. We had a birthday party. We played pin the tail on the donkey. Charlie Peno played 'Happy Birthday' on his harmonica; my dad sang along, and—just for a split second—forgot the words. Bobby circled the festivities *yarrh-yarrhing*; poor little Malka scuttled away, crying, 'Murder! God, help me!' Little Jack Horner sat in a corner, I'm-Scott-Dagleish-from-Riverview; *Miss Polly had a dolly that was sick, sick, sick*, and Warren Morris escaped.

Warren Morris—used to teach Manual Arts at All Souls School—asks my dad, 'How do you get out? I've seen you out there.' Every day, Warren Morris—physically fit as a mallee bull—asks my dad, *How do you get out? My truck's just out there.* My dad raised the alarm when Warren Morris escaped. Warren was halfway to Timbuktu in his truck when all the King's horses and all the King's men caught up with Warren Morris.

Olive's birthday party concluded with a friendly little sparring match when Alec, from the next room, got lost and climbed into *Fred and Olive's Bed* with Fred and Olive. A great time was had by all when the boys came out to play, *Georgie Porgie ran away* ...

'Can't you please put a childproof latch on Fred and Olive's door?'

'Against regulation.'

I'm leaving her tomorrow, but my mum won't know I'm gone. It's hard, watching someone you love die by slow increments. It's hard, lying with your mum in the same bed your mum's going to die in.

Mum went missing after her party. Staff weren't worried—not like my mum can fly away. My mum hasn't got her new wings yet. Some mix-up—botched paperwork—in heaven. Dad searched the gardens. Dad looked in Warren's room; Dad looked in Alec's room; Dad looked everywhere before the staff started looking.

I don't know how it could have happened. Mum had slipped past the reception desk—*There's always someone there*—and had wandered into a new ward, not yet opened. Was she frightened? Two hours my mum wandered down cold, dark corridors, alone.

'Why?' I ask Death's reflection in the mirror.

If you ask, 'What is the meaning of it all?' you will feel meaningless.

'But why?'

Follow any path long enough, you're bound to trip over some tragedy or other.

'But it's like sitting in a darkened theatre with a curtain that won't come down.'

Anticipatory grief, Death says, *dress rehearsal for the Grand Finale.*

'There's worse to come?'

Any tale followed to a natural conclusion must have an unhappy ending.

My mum's asleep: poor, sad, beautiful ruin of my mother. I listen to the soft sounds of her breathing. *Please, God, let her go!*

I'm sorry, God's not taking calls today.

Please, God! While I'm here with her.

You can try again tomorrow.

I won't be here tomorrow. I say goodbye to my dad. The last eighteen months have challenged everything he ever believed about life, himself, his role as husband and protector.

'You really must come and stay with me, Dad. Have a break. Stay as long as you like.'

Please don't! Please don't leave her! Please don't leave her here alone!

Dad turns his music up. Merle Haggard follows me down the corridor: 'Why should I be lonely?'

There's something so sad about old cowboy tunes, something
that makes you want to crawl into a ditch, and die.

*

She's got to be getting home now;
it's growing late. And Mum
will be wondering
where she
is
there light someway
on the path ahead? darkness
lurks, along the
edges
there are bars,
yellow bars that run forever
away and away into ... the
night
is growing dark;
a cicada mating memory;
moonshadow sheds time past,
passing flies
away.

Alas,
for you, poor shell,
there is no time past, passing
or to come; all tenses in the present,
one step ... one hand ... one bar ... at a time.

Here, a shadow floats—Man or Shade?
A hand on her shoulder speaks:
Time to come in now;

it's Time.

14

Eulogies are for the living; cold comfort for the dead

Wednesday, 31 October 2012

It's such a little thing to weep—
So short a thing to sigh—
And yet—by Trades—the size of these
We men and women die!

Emily Dickinson

May I begin by thanking you for coming, and welcome you to this small celebration of the life of a remarkable—a truly phenomenal woman—my mum …

Silence.
My mother is dead?
Your mother is dead—she's in the coffin behind you.
In front? A sea of faces, willing me to continue.
Breathe.
Daughter of … sister to … wife and mother …

Silence.

Remember to breathe!

Mum was known as 'Mum' by the girls who worked for her at the Tropical Cafe, and she was 'Mum' to a host of Dotswood boys and ringers from the Star ...

So, here you are, summing up the beauty of her being—having been—in the space of a page: a handful of platitudes, and a teaspoon of salt:

It breaks my heart that our beautiful Mum spent the last two years of her life in prison: imprisoned by a frail body and failing mind—and by the fence at Eventide.

On many an afternoon, Mum wanted to go home. 'It's getting late,' she'd say. 'And Mum will be wondering where I am.'

By late afternoon, her anxiety grew: 'I've got to be getting on home, now,' she'd say. 'It will be dark soon, and there might be snakes along the way.'

Those who 'believe' can imagine that the path was brightly lit with summer sunshine; there were no snakes along the way, and waiting to welcome her home were her mum, Granny Chapman, her much-loved sister, June, and her so sadly missed daughter, Robyn.

Those who don't 'believe' can rest easy in the knowledge that our darling girl, our precious Mum ... finally ... is free.

I sit down. Dad lets me put an arm around him.

*

Sunday, 28 October 2012 (three days earlier)

Phone call:

Betty: The nurses just called from Eventide.

Betty: Mum won't wake up.

Betty: Are you there?

Why won't you say it?

Betty: Pam?

Why make me say it?

Betty: Will you drive up, or fly?

*A deed begins as thought. A thought, rethought, becomes obsession—
becomes an act?*

Betty …?

Betty: She died peacefully in her sleep.

Thank you, God. Thank you!

And the wheels of the car go round and round, round and round.

We are still. It is the country slipping by: inland road, JC (Johnny
Cash) *Why Me Lord* and *Do you remember whens.* Greg's remembering going out to Billy Grubb's to buy twenty fat cows—*and they're
fat all right, those cows, all bloated dead* because Billy's overdosed
the dip with arsenic. I'm remembering Billy Grubb with half his
tongue cut out. Greg's remembering how he worked all this country
contract mustering with Blue. Blue's long dead. Greg shot him.

Greg loves life. Greg's had a life-long love affair with living.

Me? Not so much. I'm a navel watcher: I was born studying
my bellybutton.

Greg cried when I told him, 'Betty just called …'

I can't cry. *She died. She is dead. What's not to understand?*

Fifteen hundred kilometres—*the wheels of the car go round and
round.*

Betty: Where are you now?

'We're just at the Belyando Crossing—be there in two hours.'

Betty: Are you going to do the eulogy?

Eulogy? Me? 'Sorry, Betty, just no way I can do it.' *I'm just the
baby.*

My mother is dead?

Death, sitting in the corner of my eye, assures me: *Your mother is dead!*

On the outskirts of Charters Towers, we pass the new rodeo complex. I'm remembering Jan's eulogy: *Jan found contentment in her final years with an involvement in the Family Christian Church.*

Ah! Cousin Jan! Death reminisces with me. *Now that was one tough nut to crack!*

'Ladies and Gentlemen, welcome to the 1980 Charters Towers Easter Rodeo. The next competitor in the steer un-decorating needs no introduction: holder of the All Round Cowgirl title four years in a row; three-time representative of the Queensland Rodeo Team at the Sydney Royal Rodeo; member of the Australian Team at the Calgary Stampede in Canada ...'

'Listen, Dilly,' Owen says, coming up alongside the young grey mare. 'I dunno about ridin' Melody. Just been up the backyard, some of them steers look like they never seen a yard, let alone bin through one.'

'... riding a new horse today, bred from her Arab stallion, Lochinvar!'

'Come on,' Owen says. 'I'll saddle Lochy for ya.'

'She'll be right!' Jan pushes the mare past her dad.

Eric Ormond spruiks: 'Invited to compete in the Australian Champion of Champions an unprecedented eleven times—a record we won't see broken in our lifetime—here she is: ladies and gentlemen, put your hands together for Jan Alloway riding her new mare, Melody!'

Chute clangs. Steer launches. Jan spurs.

Melody bounds forward, but the steer doesn't run—it ducks back in.

The mare barrels ahead, steer T-boned on her chest.

235

The steer goes down; the mare tumbles, spearing Jan into the turf.

Tangled in a cloud of dust, horse and steer scrabble to find their feet.

They do. Jan doesn't.

Beat!

Men in big hats climb down rails, jump fences, run into the ring; loudspeaker's calling for the ambulance; audience is silent … waiting for her to move … wanting her to get up … dust herself off, wave her hat at the crowd … show them she's all right.

But she wasn't. And she didn't.

BFF, my cousin Jan was unconscious, and hooked up for weeks.

Aunty Melva and Uncle Owen were more or less told she wasn't going to make it. But she came out of it. After two months of rehab Jan checked herself out in a wheelchair, told them they could stick their hospital up their arse—she wasn't gonna have some two-bit orderly wipe her bum.

'Ladies and gentlemen, we saw her earlier this morning when her father helped her onto her stallion, Lochinvar. For those of you not here this time last year, Jan had a dreadful crash on these grounds—and in this event. This time last year, they were saying she wouldn't talk again; this time last year, they were saying she wouldn't walk again, but here she is: a big warm round of applause for the winner of the 1981 Easter Rodeo Steer Un-decorating Competition—a rodeo legend in her own time: Jan Alloway!'

BFF, my cousin Jan.

I remember, too, Aunty Melva telling me how the old brain injury caused Jan to fit. And how Jan Alloway, rodeo legend in her own time, had a fit and drowned in a rain puddle in her own backyard. And how her son, Bradley, found her.

I reach over, turn off JC.

We pass 38 Mount Leyshon Road. My first home. Pergola's gone. Dad's white picket fence, red verandas and coloured stepping stones are still there. House looks tiny. *Just Ollie and me, and baby makes three ...* Seven of the eight royal palms Dad showed the bankman half a century ago—*like policemen directing traffic*—now tower above the house.

Nothing is clear, just a confusion of regrets. *I should have been with her.*

Aussie Outback Oasis, home away from home, is fully booked tonight.

Outside the Dalrymple Caravan Park on a chalkboard: *Quote of the Day: Don't worry about the destination; enjoy the journey!*

Justify the journey? Reconcile the past? *Dad, did you do it?*

15

Truth is like a bellybutton: each man has his own

October 2012

Dad: I'm not going. Why should I sit with a bunch of hypocrites? Not one of them came to visit her in the last two years. Not one.

Dad came. Funeral was nice. Church was full. Friends—*who hadn't been to visit in two years*—crawled out of the woodwork. I'm glad they came. I don't blame them.

Aunty Dulcie, oldest of the sisters, still going strong, just a little bit forgetful now ...

Aunty Melva, youngest of the sisters, in a wheelchair ...

Greg's daughter, Mia Elizabeth, with little Lily Robyn in her arms—two-year-old Ben has stayed at home with his dad. Greg's other daughter, Deborah May, can't be here; she's in Ireland.

Lots of cousins.

Thank you. Thank you for coming.

I watch myself deliver lines: *Yes, in the end, it was a blessing.*

I watch myself deliver the eulogy—lots of silences, tears streaming.

Wouldn't have managed if I hadn't cornered the Eventide doctor. 'Can you prescribe me some beta blockers?' Doctor said nothing, looked at me over his glasses. 'I really want to say a few words at my mum's funeral, but …'

Next door to the new church is the old Holy Family Anglican Church. Robyn and Greg were married there. It's an op shop now. Robyn was so beautiful I had to wipe my nose on my glove. I love op shops. *Outfit by Vinnies:* bought my black dress and shoes there this morning. Cost six dollars, all up. A shrink might say it's my father's voice—and his father's before him—competing for expression. Maybe Granny Chapman's voice? *Look after the pennies and the pounds will look after themselves.* Don't think about the coffin, look instead at the photo of Mum and Dad at the White Falls, 1948.

My darling little mum—took two years to die—got a eulogy typed in haste at five o'clock in the morning. This woman who gave all and asked for nothing in return, got what she asked for. Selflessness has a price.

So here am I, Dad sitting in the corner of my eye, sorting garbage. 'No,' Dad tells me. 'I didn't do it.'

Thank you, God!

The Fred Bagnall Park sign still hasn't arrived from Melbourne. *Paperwork.*

Who cares? Stick your park sign up your arse.

I'm moving my dad back up into the clusters. *Regulations.*

Can't smash *Regulation* in the face; *Regulation*'s got no face to smash.

Tomorrow, we'll go up to Betty's shop. Front security screen will be smashed, chocolates and cigarettes stolen; hairdresser next door broken into too.

While we wait for the police, I'll ask, 'Have her ashes arrived yet, Betty?'

Betty will glance at Dad; quick shake of her head, warning me to silence.

Later, Betty will tell me: 'They took her ashes. They were here, on the counter.'

Mental snort: *Someone has stolen my mum's ashes?*

Mum's ashes, posted from Townsville: unwrapped package on the counter. Final expression of a world gone mad: *Someone has stolen my mum's ashes?*

Final indignity for my mum: her ashes, lying somewhere in a gutter.

Fuck you, God!

Greg will spend all day searching the grounds of Eventide—*They'll throw them away, when they realise*—and searching the bins in the park across the road.

It's pointless. This morning was garbage pick-up.

It's pointless, but I'll follow Greg's tracks in the afternoon—*just in case*—and lift the lid on every stinking, empty, wheelie bin in the park across the road looking for my mother.

Sorry, she's gone out with the garbage.

Fuck you, God!

'Dad, can I have some of your bicarb of soda?' *Tink-a-tink-a-tink*, burp.

So here am I, sorting garbage, detritus of my mother's life, looking for a Sign: something ... anything ... to tell me that she knows I'm here, that *I'm so sorry.*

And if her soul could speak to me, would she?

Please forgive me, Mum.

No Sign, only memories.

A biscuit tin of yellowing cards: this card is new; this card is edged in silver and embossed with two doves holding up a heart-shaped garland of roses. Inside the heart, printed in matte embossed silver, *Olive and Fred—65th Wedding Anniversary.*

Sixty-fifth anniversary congratulation messages: the Queen; the Governor-General, and the Governor of Queensland.

I remember how they celebrated their fiftieth anniversary at the RSL hall where Dad started and ran the ANZAC concert every year. I remember how, at the RSL hall with seventy friends and relatives, Mum and Dad sang: 'We belong together, you and me.' 'You and Me'—it would always be *their* song.

They celebrated their sixty-fifth with their friends at Raintree—and Betty.

Congratulation messages for Dad turning ninety-five. A hundred sympathy cards and telegrams for Granny Chapman's passing, which Mum has kept for forty years. Who will keep them now? And for what purpose? And here's Mum's scrapbook; Betty typed it up for her. There's one loose leaf of writing paper, slipped into a sleeve, Mum's scrawly handwriting:

My Diary: 17th March, 2004
On this day, 17th of March, 1944 was the first day I became really happy, it was a long time ago. I have been happy ever since. It was my very first kiss and Fred's first slap in the face.

On their sixtieth anniversary, they re-enacted that first night. Here's the photo of Mum and Dad at Spargo's gate. It's a great photo. Looks real: Mum taking a swing at Dad, and Dad flinching away. *Dad, it would break her heart if for one second she thought you didn't love her anymore.* I never saw them fight, don't think they ever did. I've seen Dad turn his back on an argument—and, behind his back, Mum jerk her thumb at him: *Up ya bum!*

My mum didn't write history books or win Australia Day Awards, but ask her three daughters: *Which one of you girls was your mother's favourite?* Each one of us would step forward. That was Mum's special talent.

A page of creased paper caught at the back of a drawer. Difference between being a good story and telling one?

When I was young, I never expected to get married. I knew very few young people, and then met Olive Chapman. But I was a woodcutter and she was a squatter's daughter. We first met on the 17th of March, 1944. When her father was in hospital with a broken leg, I walked her home. I kissed her and she slapped me, and I thought what else would she do? After all, I was ten years older than her, and she was only 16.

However, in 1945 when she was 18, I was invited to her birthday at Fletcherview. I was never more embarrassed in all my life, sitting between Olive and her best friend, Betty Philipson.

Two years later, we were married at St Gabriels, and God gave us three lovely daughters. I would never have lived only for the great assistance I have received from Olive, Robyn, Betty and Pam.

Our worst year was 2004, when Olive had several operations and a stroke, and then Robyn died at Coolum.

And 2005 has not started off any better when Olive smashed her car.

What can the future bring?

Fred Bagnall, March 2005

Last drawer, bottom drawer, is empty. But at the back I find two treasures: a thumb-sized bottle—piece of Granddad Dick's shinbone; both bottle and bone yellow with age.

And my mum's top dentures.

I slip Granddad Dick into my bag. I close the drawer on my mum's teeth.

Tomorrow someone—someone who won't think twice—can throw them in the bin.

*

November 2012

Confession: the need to gain forgiveness from those sanctioned to absolve.

There's a black hole in my head.

Around a black hole there is an area called an *event horizon*; it marks the point of no return.

You were going to insist he come and live with you.

I don't offer. He doesn't ask. 'Nice knowing you,' he said, when I left him.

How can you leave him, an old man sitting alone outside Fred's Room?

How can I not?

At Aussie Outback Oasis I lie listening to the tremors of disparate selves and contradictory voices: Go to him. *He'll already be asleep.* Go to him and hold him. *His door will be locked.* Go to him. *Can't drive.* Go to him.

It's too late.

He'll have taken a sleeping pill; door will be locked, and you don't want a DUI.

We're sitting in Betty's shop; Greg's looking for my mother's ashes that Dad doesn't know are missing. I'm leaving tomorrow, and Dad, hands folded on his walking stick, has called a family meeting: Betty and me.

I raise a finger at my dad: 'Don't say it!' Finger raised, voice raised, I repeat, 'Don't say it!' First time in my life I have raised my voice to my father. 'Don't say it!'

'Say what?' Betty looks at us confused.

'Don't say it!' *Please don't say it!*

Dad, forehead leaned on hands on walking stick, says it anyway: *I did it.*

I don't offer. *How can you leave him there, alone?* He doesn't ask.

We all pray for the dawn, in the hope that we will wake in peace, without memory of pain; where there'd been anguish there will be calm …

Oh, Dad.

16

Every terror that haunted me has caught up with me

... And all that I fear has come upon me.
There is no peace of mind or quiet for me;
I chafe in torment and have no rest.

3:24–26, New English Bible

Clermont: 10 November 2012

'What's wrong, matey?'

'Nothing.' *Only ... there's a black hole in my head.* 'Why?'

'Your mouth's going ten to the dozen.'

Overnight, I've become one of those poor old ladies who walk around muttering to themselves, *Murder! God help me!*

Greg's listening to some 'poor old dirt farmer' ...

I try to conjure Whitney Houston—she's been helpful in the past—but Whitney won't play for me. And now the poor old dirt farmer's gone and fallen off his tractor ...

Dumb song.

Email: From Betty B
Subject: Dad

How are you going? Please let me know you are okay, Betty.

Me: I respect your decision to support him, Betty—I don't/ can't.

Betty: Pam, you have to let it go. Mum died peacefully in her sleep and that's what you have to remember. She certainly did not have any quality of life. You need to think of Dad now as he is the one who is suffering.

Greg's driving.

I'm muttering at my reflection in the glass: blurred, transient, shifting—superimposed on shadowy scenes rushing by outside. *Symptoms of Acute Stress Disorder typically include an initial state of 'daze'.* Announcements of destinations, arrivals and departures echo along the highway: *Emerald … Springsure … Injune … Roma for the night.*

I fear the night; the night seeps in: grainy newsreel, speckled sepia, poorly cut and flickering. No familiar faces; strangers loom in close-up.

Last night, consumed by his pain, I cried for my dad.

Tonight there's a place, deep inside, where there are no tears, just a void sucking inward. Tonight, thoughts too deep for tears reach the point of no return: fearsome keening from another dimension regurgitating guilt—*You did nothing to stop it!* Memory spewing uninvited ghosts, constructing parallel universes: *could have, would have, should have*; pain, purging all before it, leaves nothing in its wake. *Forgive me, Mum.*

Grief distilled: *He wants to have me put down like a dog!*

That's what my mum said when we walked into the tail end of his interview with Nathalie Fernbach of the ABC ... *she just goes and stares into space ... she doesn't hear anything ... or anything ...*

Mum heard. And Mum understood: *He wants to have me put down like a dog!*

Had she the wings to fly away ...

Don't say it! Say what? Say that you had something to do with Mum's death.

Had I the wings to flee from: *I did it.*

I would be that person smiling beatifically: *She died peacefully in her sleep.*

I don't want to be this person: *My father killed my mother? Dad killed Mum?*

I want to be that person, smiling beatifically: *So in the end, you see, it was a blessing.*

Despair too deep to plumb: *You bastard! You ... fucking ... bastard!*

I don't want to be this person: *You bastard! You ... fucking ... fucking bastard!*

This is who I am: *You ... fucking ... fucking ... fucking ... CUNT!*

Heart so empty, it must surely burst.

And the world moves on. Surat, Moonie, Goondiwindi.

Email: From Betty B
Sent: Wednesday, 14 November 2012
Subject: Dad

Bob rang today to say the park sign still hasn't left Melbourne but it should get here by next Wednesday. Maybe.

Me: I don't give a fuck about his park. You know I only

started the whole thing to give him an interest: some reason to keep him going—so he wouldn't kill himself—or Mum.

Betty: I am glad you spoke to Dad. He said, 'No, she doesn't want to talk to me' when I handed him the phone. I have to point out that we both knew Dad had tablets. Neither of us took the tablets away, which can only mean we were happy for him to use them. Remember we have actively helped him in the battle for euthanasia, this might not have been the way we wanted it applied, but it was still the same thing.

Me: I've always supported him on euthanasia, but always with the proviso that it was for himself—no one else.

Betty: But he always said it was so they could go together. Please forgive him and talk with him or you will always regret it when he does go.

Me: So why the fuck didn't he kill himself with her?

Betty: Not to be callous, but yes I do sometimes wish he had taken the rest of the tablets and hoped they did the trick, but then it might not have worked and we would have been left with a murder–suicide investigation and all that goes with it. It was only his great love for her that made him act that way. I am very happy for Mum that she has escaped a prolonged stay in Raintree—or worse being bedridden and transferred to Tamarind—I could tell you a hundred horror stories from the other wards. Just have some compassion for Dad, as he is hurting badly, and think how distressing it has been for him to watch Mum slipping away more each week. He wrote a letter to the *Townsville Bulletin* explaining what he'd done. I wouldn't post it for him. He's still not eating. No wonder I'm going grey. As it stands only you and I (Greg?) know.

Me: Greg doesn't know. I can't tell him. Why did Dad tell us? We were all so happy that she'd died peacefully in her sleep.

Betty: She did die peacefully in her sleep.

17

The living years

19 November 2012

'Hello, Dad, I'm going to write about it. Why? Well, you wanted some sort of platform for euthanasia, and I can't talk to a shrink. No, I won't come up for the opening of the Fred Bagnall Park—if I don't write about it, I'll disappear up my own bellybutton—but I'll come up at Christmas and you can help me with my book …

'Tell me again, about the first time you met Mum …'

It's hard loving someone by phone when you don't know who they are.

15 December 2012

'Hello, Dad. Can't talk this afternoon. I'm on the road, and the reception is no good.'

Dad: Okay. Goodbye.

Goodbye? He always finishes, *Thank you for calling.*

Doesn't matter, I'll be up there next week.

16 December 2012

Y.o.u h.a.v.e o.n.e n.e.w m.e.s.s.a.g.e: m.e.s.s.a.g.e r.e.c.e.i.v.e.d t.o.d.a.y. at 9…46 am: 'Yeah, it's Betty, call me back …'

Betty slapped Regulation in the face with a DNR.

Killing yourself is not easy—or painless? Spasms, leakages, gasping for breath: mind imploring Death; body imploring Life. His death was not unspeakably grim, but the eighteen-hour image in my mind is far from winged angels.

Spare me the untidy mechanics of his dying?

Old man moves centre stage. Expires. Fade. Curtain.
Frederick Francis Bagnall: b. 06.06.1917 d. 16.12.2012

There you have it. My fingers tap the keys and it is done: my dad is dead.

Mike and the Mechanics' 'The Living Years' on loop … I could tell you how the church was full, but emotion overrides intellect—you can't see clearly when your eyes are full of tears. I could tell you how a politician sidled up to Greg: *Did he …? You know, did he?* (I'm glad Greg didn't deck him—but I wouldn't have minded if he did.) I could tell you how they had a big procession down the main street, and how all the staff at Eventide came out and lined the road; but from all these keystrokes—black on white—one sentence returns to haunt me: *Fred will look after Ollie …*

Granny Chapman was a wise old bird.

Epilogue

Mum's birthday: 31 July 2013

On the outskirts of Charters Towers you'll find the Venus Gold Battery. Built in 1872, it is the largest surviving battery relic in Australia and the oldest surviving battery in Queensland. Although the battery ceased commercial operations nearly half a century ago, in its gaunt remains you will catch a glimpse of the real-life gold-rush days of a city that was once called 'The World'.

Facing the Venus Battery is a small park, redolent with gum leaves, sunshine rippling on clear water.

The official plaque on the Fred Bagnall Park sign reads:

Fred Bagnall
Local Historian
Citizen of the Year, 2008

Behind the official plaque, on the Fred Bagnall Park sign, someone has commissioned another plaque:

Behind every good man is a good woman:
Olive May Bagnall (nee Chapman).
Married 65 years.

On the 31st of July 2013—what would have been Olive's eighty-sixth birthday—Betty Bowen and Bob Read bore witness to the marriage of Pamela and Gregory Parker at the Fred Bagnall Park.

Those who *believe* know that Olive and Fred Bagnall—together with Granny Chapman and Robyn Parker (nee Bagnall)—were also present at the celebration.

For those who don't *believe*, Mum says: *Up ya bum!*

Acknowledgements

I would like to thank:

Ita Buttrose AO OBE—her belief that *The Long Goodbye* 'should be published' gave me the courage to persevere.

Mary Cunnane for seeing 'something rather special' in *The Long Goodbye*; Alex Adsett of Alex Adsett Literary Agency/Publishing Services for giving me contract advice.

The Hardie Grant team—especially Publishing Director Fran Berry and Senior Development Editor Meelee Soorkia—for bringing *The Long Goodbye* to the public. Thanks also to editor Emma Schwarcz for her patience and attention to detail, and to Nikki Lusk for her excellent suggestions.

Dr Anna Donald for her talent, wit and dry good humour.

Margaret Kennedy (Deputy Principal Trinity Anglican School, Cairns) and my Tenterfield friends, Christine Clark and Mary Warwick (Tenterfield Writers' Ink) for their encouragement during the drafting process.

My dear sister, Betty Bowen, for her on-going support—and for her brilliant memory of dates, places and events.

And finally, my *'the glass is three quarters full'* person, Greg Parker—husband, friend and confidante—for believing in me.

About the author

Pamela J. Parker was born and raised in the once famous gold-mining town of Charters Towers in rural Queensland, Australia. She was educated locally before attending James Cook University in Townsville and later Queensland University in Brisbane where she studied to become a teacher. Pamela has taught at schools throughout Northern Queensland. After raising cattle and training horses in Tenterfield, New South Wales, Pamela and her husband, Greg, are now retired and living in Caloundra.

Olive and Fred, 1946